MATH TRAILBLAZERS™

Grade
4

Unit Resource Guide
Unit 4
Products and Factors

SECOND EDITION

A Mathematical Journey Using Science and Language Arts

KENDALL/HUNT PUBLISHING COMPANY
4050 Westmark Drive   Dubuque, Iowa 52002

A TIMS® Curriculum
University of Illinois at Chicago

UIC The University of Illinois
at Chicago

The original edition was based on work supported by the National Science Foundation under grant No. MDR 9050226 and the University of Illinois at Chicago. Any opinions, findings, and conclusions or recommendations expressed in this publication are those of the author(s) and do not necessarily reflect the views of the granting agencies.

LETTER HOME

Products and Factors

Date: _____

Dear Family Member:

We are beginning a new unit in math called *Products and Factors.* We will explore multiplication and division by looking at ways objects can be put into arrays. An array is a collection of objects arranged in rows. Things that come in arrays can be counted by multiplication. For example, an auditorium that has 20 rows with 10 seats in each row has 20 × 10 seats.

We will investigate the different sizes of arrays that are possible with certain numbers of objects. For example, we can arrange 20 objects into four rows, but not into three rows. This will naturally lead us to explore the relationship between multiplication and division, as well as to practice with the multiplication facts.

Students arrange tiles in rows as they learn about multiplication and division.

You can help your child with multiplication using the following ideas:

• Flash cards for the multiplication facts for the 2s and 3s will be sent home. Help your child study the 2s and the 3s by using the flash cards.

• Your child will learn some words in this unit such as factor and multiple. Ask your child what these words mean. He or she will also learn about some special numbers such as prime numbers and square numbers. Ask about these. You might also ask your child to explain why the square numbers (4, 9, 16, etc.) are called "square."

Sincerely,

_____

UNIT OUTLINE

Products and Factors

Pacing Suggestions

Lesson 6 *Multiplying to Solve Problems* is an optional lesson. These problems can be assigned as homework throughout the unit or solved in class. Since the lesson requires little teacher preparation, it is appropriate to leave for a substitute teacher.

Components Key: SG = Student Guide, DAB = Discovery Assignment Book, AB = Adventure Book, URG = Unit Resource Guide, and DPP = Daily Practice and Problems

	Sessions	Description	Supplies
LESSON 1 **Multiplication and Rectangles** SG pages 96–101 DAB page 45 URG pages 22–34 DPP A–F	3	**ACTIVITY:** Students investigate the dimensions of rectangles that can be made with a specified number of square-inch tiles. They use their rectangles to investigate multiples, prime numbers, and square numbers. Using exponents to write square numbers is introduced.	• square-inch tiles • easel paper or construction paper • tape • scissors • envelopes
LESSON 2 **Factors** SG pages 102–106 URG pages 35–45 DPP G–J	2	**ACTIVITY:** Using rectangular arrays of square-inch tiles, students discuss factors and prime numbers.	• square-inch tiles • calculators
LESSON 3 **Floor Tiler** SG pages 107–108 DAB page 47 URG pages 46–50 DPP K–L	1	**GAME:** Students play a game that provides practice with the multiplication facts. After using spinners to find two numbers, a player uses the product of the two numbers to color in rectangles on grid paper. Players take turns spinning and filling in rectangles until someone completely fills in his or her grid.	• paper clips and pencils or clear plastic spinners • crayons or markers • calculators • scissors
LESSON 4 **Prime Factors** SG pages 109–115 URG pages 51–62 DPP M–R	3–4	**ACTIVITY:** Students use factor trees to find the prime factorization of numbers. They use exponents as a shortcut for writing repeated factors. **ASSESSMENT PAGE:** *Unit 4 Test,* Unit Resource Guide, pages 58–59.	• calculators • square-inch tiles

	Sessions	Description	Supplies
LESSON 5			
Product Bingo **SG** pages 116–117 **DAB** page 49 **URG** pages 63–69 **DPP** S–T	1	**GAME:** Students use two spinners to generate multiplication problems. They find the products and place markers showing the products on a bingo card. Players find that one card is most likely to win because more of its numbers can be obtained as products in several ways.	• paper clips and pencils or clear plastic spinners • game markers
LESSON 6		– OPTIONAL ACTIVITY –	
Multiplying to Solve Problems **SG** page 118 **URG** pages 70–73	1	**OPTIONAL ACTIVITY:** Students solve a variety of word problems on content from this and previous units.	• calculators • square-inch tiles

CONNECTIONS

A current list of connections is available at www.mathtrailblazers.com.

Literature

Suggested Title

■ Hulme, Joy N. *Sea Squares.* Illustrated by Carol Schwartz. Hyperion Books for Children, New York, 1993.

Software

■ *Math Arena* is a collection of math activities that reinforces many math concepts.

■ *Mighty Math Calculating Crew* poses short answer questions about number operations and money skills.

■ *Mighty Math Number Heroes* poses short answer questions about fractions, number operations, polygons, and probability.

■ *Math Munchers Deluxe* provides practice with basic facts, factors, and multiples in an arcade-like game.

■ *Math Mysteries: Advanced Whole Numbers* is a series of structured multistep word problems dealing with whole numbers.

■ *National Library of Virtual Manipulatives* website (http://matti.usu.edu) allows students to work with manipulatives including rectangle multiplication.

■ *Number Sense—Puzzle Tanks* develops logical thinking while practicing math facts.

■ *Schoolhouse Rock!* develops number sense, math facts, and geometry skills.

BACKGROUND

Products and Factors

In this unit, students work with the array model for multiplication and investigate factors of numbers. Students begin by exploring the dimensions of rectangular arrays of tiles that can be made with a specified number of square-inch tiles. This leads naturally to an investigation of the factors and multiples of numbers and to the study of special numbers such as prime numbers and square numbers. After finding factor pairs of several numbers, students are challenged to find prime factors. Factor trees help students organize their work. Exponents are introduced as a shortcut for writing products of repeated factors.

In third grade, students developed strategies for learning the multiplication facts. A review of the multiplication facts began in fourth grade in Unit 3. Students also began developing strategies for learning the related division facts through the study of fact families. In this unit, the multiplication facts for the twos and the threes are practiced and assessed and the division facts are introduced through the Daily Practice and Problems and Home Practice.

The work with factors in this unit gives students an opportunity to explore the relationship between multiplication and division, as well as to practice working with the multiplication and division facts. An algorithm for multiplying two-digit by one-digit numbers is introduced in Unit 7 and extended to larger numbers in Unit 11. For more information on multiplication, see the TIMS Tutors: *Math Facts* and *Arithmetic* in the *Teacher Implementation Guide*.

Array Model of Multiplication

The first situation in which students encountered multiplication in third grade involved objects arranged in equal-sized groups, as in Figure 1. They learned that the number of objects in 5 groups of 6 objects is 5×6. The product can be found by repeated addition: $5 \times 6 = 6 + 6 + 6 + 6 + 6$.

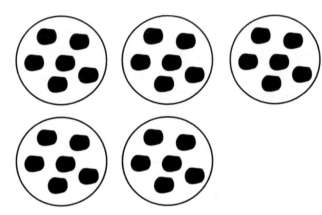

Figure 1: *5 groups of 6 cookies*

In this unit we look at arrays as another model for multiplication. An **array** is an arrangement of elements into a rectangular pattern of (horizontal) rows and (vertical) columns. For example, a candy box that contains 5 rows with 6 pieces in each row is a 5×6 array. The array model of multiplication is just a special case of the equal grouping model, where the rows of the array are the groups. Thus, the number of objects in 5 rows of 6 objects, for instance, is 5×6. One virtue of the array model is that by rotating the array, one can see very clearly that $5 \times 6 = 6 \times 5$. Another advantage is that it creates a visual image of a multiplication problem.

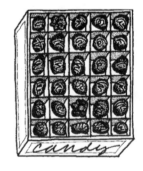

Figure 2: *From left to right, a 5 × 6 array and a 6 × 5 array*

Just as many things naturally come in groups, there are many things that naturally come in arrays. For example, eggs in a carton, candy in a box, soda cans in a six-pack, panes in a window, and ice cubes in a tray all come in arrays. Recognizing arrays when they occur helps students recognize problems that can be solved by multiplication.

Division

Two distinct types of division situations are encountered in this unit. In both types, a set of objects is divided into equal-sized groups. In one type of division situation, sometimes called *equal sharing* or **partitive division,** the number of groups (partitions) and the total number of objects in the set are known. The number in each group is found by division. This is reflected in problems such as the following:

> Twelve cookies were divided equally among four children. How many cookies did each child get? ($12 \div 4 = 3$)

> Thirty seats in a classroom were arranged in five rows. How many seats were in each row? ($30 \div 5 = 6$)

Problems of this type can be solved by "dealing out" the objects to the groups, for example, to the students or into the rows.

In the other type of division situation, sometimes called *equal grouping* or **measurement division,** the number in each group (the measure of the group) and the total number of objects in the set are known. Division is used to find the number of groups. This is reflected in problems like the following:

> Twelve cookies were put onto plates, with three cookies on each plate. How many plates of cookies were there?

> Thirty seats in a classroom were arranged into rows. Each row had six seats. How many rows were there?

Problems of this type can be solved by making groups of a specific size. This type of division is also known as subtractive because the process can be seen as repeated subtraction of a specific number.

Students need to be presented with examples of both types of division problems, although they do not need to identify them by name.

Division Symbols

There are several different symbols that are commonly used to denote division. The quantity "32 divided by 4" can be represented as:

(a) $32 \div 4 = 8$ (b) $32/4 = 8$

(c) $\frac{32}{4} = 8$ (d) $4\overline{)32}$ with 8 above

Each of these sentences can be read as "32 divided by 4 is 8," "4 divided into 32 is 8," "4 goes into 32 eight times," or "there are 8 fours in 32." It is important that students learn to read and write division sentences properly. The order of the numbers does make a difference. A common mistake, for example, is to read the division in (d) as "4 divided by 32." But, "4 divided by 32" is $32\overline{)4}$ whose value is $\frac{4}{32}$ or $\frac{1}{8}$. In *Math Trailblazers*™, we use a variety of methods for displaying division sentences. Exposure to a variety of methods and symbols will prepare students for different experiences with division.

Prime Numbers

A whole number is a **prime number** if it has no factors other than itself and one. All other (whole) numbers larger than one are called **composite numbers** and can be expressed as products of prime numbers. In that sense, prime numbers are the building blocks from which all other whole numbers are multiplicatively made. Because of this, the prime numbers have been the subject of much study. Around 300 BCE, the Greek scholar Euclid proved that there are infinitely many prime numbers. Although there is no quick way to test whether a number is prime, computers have made it possible to produce long lists of prime numbers. However, there are many unanswered questions. A sample of the kinds of questions mathematicians ask about prime numbers includes the following:

> Some pairs of prime numbers, such as 3 and 5, 11 and 13, and 29 and 31, are only two apart. These are called *twin primes*. Are there infinitely many twin primes? No one knows the answer.

> Many numbers are the sum of a square number and a prime number. For example, $19 = 16 + 3$ and $14 = 9 + 5$. Is this true for all numbers from some point on? Again, no one knows the answer.

Resources

- Bennett, Albert B., Jr. and L. Ted Nelson. *Mathematics for Elementary Teachers: A Conceptual Approach*. McGraw Hill, Boston, 2001.
- Burns, Marilyn. *A Collection of Math Lessons from Grades 3 through 6*. Math Solution Publications, New York, 1987.
- *Mathematics for the Young Child*. National Council of Teachers of Mathematics, Reston, VA, 1990.
- Post, Thomas R. (ed.) *Teaching Mathematics in Grades K through 8: Research-Based Methods*. Allyn and Bacon, Boston, 1992.

  And for more on prime numbers, see:
- Eves, Howard. *An Introduction to the History of Mathematics*. The Saunders Series, Harcourt Brace Jovanovich College Publishers, New York, 1990.
- http://www.utm.edu/research/primes/largest.html

Assessment Indicators

- Can students represent multiplication and division problems using arrays?
- Can students determine whether one number is a multiple of another number?
- Can students determine whether one number is a factor of another number?
- Can students identify prime, composite, and square numbers?
- Can students find the prime factorization of a number?
- Can students explain their mathematical reasoning?
- Do students demonstrate fluency with the multiplication math facts for the 2s and 3s?
- Can students write the four number sentences in the fact families for the 2s and 3s?

OBSERVATIONAL ASSESSMENT RECORD

(A1) Can students represent multiplication and division problems using arrays?

(A2) Can students determine whether one number is a multiple of another number?

(A3) Can students determine whether one number is a factor of another number?

(A4) Can students identify prime, composite, and square numbers?

(A5) Can students find the prime factorization of a number?

(A6) Can students explain their mathematical reasoning?

(A7) Do students demonstrate fluency with the multiplication math facts for the 2s and 3s?

(A8) Can students write the four number sentences in the fact families for the 2s and 3s?

(A9) _____

Name	A1	A2	A3	A4	A5	A6	A7	A8	A9	Comments
1.										
2.										
3.										
4.										
5.										
6.										
7.										
8.										
9.										
10.										
11.										
12.										
13.										

Name	A1	A2	A3	A4	A5	A6	A7	A8	A9	Comments
14.										
15.										
16.										
17.										
18.										
19.										
20.										
21.										
22.										
23.										
24.										
25.										
26.										
27.										
28.										
29.										
30.										
31.										
32.										

4 Daily Practice and Problems

Products and Factors

Two DPP items are included for each non-optional class session listed in the Unit Outline. The first item is always a Bit and the second is either a Task or a Challenge. Refer to the Daily Practice and Problems and Home Practice Guide in the *Teacher Implementation Guide* for further information on the DPP. A Scope and Sequence Chart for the DPP for the year can be found in the Scope and Sequence Chart & the NCTM *Principles and Standards* section of the *Teacher Implementation Guide*.

A DPP Menu for Unit 4

Eight icons designate the subject matter of the DPP items. Each DPP item falls into one or more of the categories listed below. A brief menu of the DPP items in Unit 4 follows.

N Number Sense	**☒** Computation	**⏲** Time	**⊟** Geometry
B, J, K, N, O, R, T	C, D, F, I, J, M–P	I, Q, T	H, L
⁵ₓ⁷ Math Facts	**$** Money	**▥** Measurement	**▨** Data
A–C, E–G, J–M, R, S	J, N	H, L, Q	T

Calculations: Paper and Pencil, Calculators, Mental Math, or Estimation?

The DPP provides many opportunities for practice of computational skills. Practice of paper-and-pencil calculations and mental math is emphasized throughout the DPP. The directions for items designed to develop these skills will indicate when the use of calculators is not appropriate. It is important, however, that students have access to calculators for all other items. Students need many opportunities in which they must decide whether it makes most sense to use paper-and-pencil procedures, calculators, mental math, or estimation. Items C, F, J, and P for this unit involve computation and provide students with examples of such situations. In order to make an appropriate choice of method, students must first step back and consider the problem thoughtfully, identifying what it is asking and what information is given. Developing this habit will help students determine which operations to employ and which methods or tools will be most efficient, thereby saving much time and frustration in the long run. The following paragraphs describe appropriate methods of computation students may choose for some of these items.

- Item C, also a math facts item, contains the problem 3×200 and asks students to solve it using mental math. Solving this problem using the math fact, 3×2, or skip counting 200, 400, 600, are both effective mental math strategies.

- Item F involves both a problem that can be solved efficiently using mental math (3×3 or skip counting 3, 6, 9) and a problem that is most appropriately solved using a calculator (18×65). Since students have not developed fluency with a multiplication algorithm yet, they will need a calculator to solve this problem.

- To solve *Question 1* in item J, students may use a combination of strategies such as mental math and paper-and-pencil computations. Students might mentally compute the cost of the tickets for the adults (2×6) but use mental math or calculators to find the cost for the children ($3 \times \$4.50$). *Question 2* in item J is a multistep problem involving addition, subtraction, and multiplication. Using a calculator to solve this problem is appropriate.

- *Questions 1A–1D* in item P provide students with paper-and-pencil practice for multidigit addition and subtraction. Note that the directions tell students to use paper-and-pencil or mental math strategies. Students are also encouraged to estimate answers to these problems to check the reasonableness of their answers. To solve *Question 1D* (34,500 – 4003), students may use paper-and-pencil procedures, but subtracting across zeros is difficult and not particularly efficient. Subtracting 4000 from 34,500 gives 30,500. Counting back 3, gives 30,497.

Before students complete DPP items, discuss the possible strategies for particular problems and whether it is appropriate to use a calculator or another method of calculating and why. For more information on helping students choose appropriate strategies for computation, see the TIMS Tutor: *Arithmetic* in the *Teacher Implementation Guide*.

The Multiplication and Division Facts

By the end of fourth grade, students in *Math Trailblazers* are expected to demonstrate fluency with all the multiplication and division facts. The DPP for this unit continues the systematic, strategies-based approach to practicing the multiplication facts and learning the division facts through the use of fact families and other strategies. This unit focuses on the second group of facts, the twos and threes.

The *Triangle Flash Cards: 2s* and *3s* follow the Home Practice for this unit in the *Discovery Assignment Book*. In Grade 4, students use the flash cards to practice the multiplication facts through Unit 8. In Units 9 through 16, students use the *Triangle Flash Cards* to practice the division facts. Bit A of the DPP for Unit 4 contains instructions for using the *Triangle Flash Cards* and the *Multiplication Facts I Know* chart. DPP Bit S is a quiz on the twos and threes multiplication facts. Other items listed under the Math Facts icon in the DPP menu provide practice using the multiplication and division facts for the twos and threes.

For more information about the distribution and assessment of the math facts, see the TIMS Tutor: *Math Facts* in the *Teacher Implementation Guide*. Also refer to the DPP guide in the *Unit Resource Guide* for Unit 3.

Daily Practice and Problems

Students may solve the items individually, in groups, or as a class. The items may also be assigned for homework.

Student Questions	Teacher Notes

 Triangle Flash Cards: 2s and 3s

With a partner, use your *Triangle Flash Cards* to quiz each other on the multiplication facts involving twos and threes. One partner covers the shaded corner (containing the highest number). This number will be the answer to a multiplication fact called the product. The second person multiplies the two other numbers, one of which is circled and the other is in a square. These two are the factors.

Separate the used cards into three piles: those facts you know and can answer quickly, those that you can figure out with a strategy, and those that you need to learn. Practice the last two piles again and then make a list of the facts you need to practice at home for homework.

Circle the facts you know and can answer quickly on your *Multiplication Facts I Know* chart.

TIMS Bit

The *Triangle Flash Cards* follow the Home Practice for this unit in the *Discovery Assignment Book*. Part 1 of the Home Practice reminds students to bring the list of the facts they need to practice home for homework. The *Triangle Flash Cards* should also be sent home.

Have students circle the facts they know well on their *Multiplication Facts I Know* charts. Remind students that if they know a fact, they also know its turn-around fact. Since these charts can also be used as multiplication tables, students should have them available to use as needed.

Inform students when the quiz on the twos and threes will be given. This quiz appears in TIMS Bit S.

Pattern Triangle

Look at the triangle and answer the following questions.

1. Describe any patterns in the rows (across).

2. Do the diagonal columns show any patterns?

3. Complete the last row of the triangle.

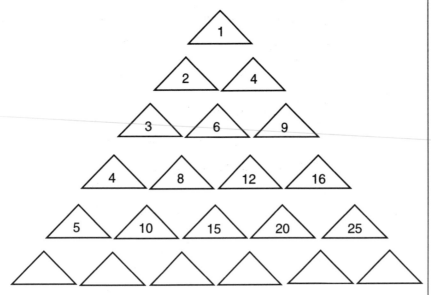

TIMS Task

1. Counting by 2s, 3s, 4s, then 5s; The third row has multiples of 3, etc.

2. First diagonal column moving down to the left is counting by ones, second column starts with 4 and counts on by twos, etc. The last or rightmost diagonal column moving down to the right is made up of square numbers. Students may see other patterns.

3. 6, 12, 18, 24, 30, 36

 Using Twos

Do these problems in your head. Write only the answers.

A. $2 \times 9 =$ B. $3 \times 200 =$

C. $2 \times 1000 =$ D. $8 \times 2 =$

E. $5 \times 20 =$ F. $20 \times 2 =$

G. $40 \times 2 =$ H. $6 \times 2 =$

I. $2 \times 7 =$ J. $0 \times 2 =$

TIMS Bit

Ask students what strategies they use for solving these problems.

A. 18   B. 600

C. 2000   D. 16

E. 100   F. 40

G. 80   H. 12

I. 14   J. 0

Student Questions	Teacher Notes

 What's Missing?

The letter *n* stands for a missing number. What number must *n* be to make each number sentence true?

1. $30 + 24 = n$
2. $n - 8 = 9$
3. $n - 20 = 33$
4. $15 + n = 21$
5. $11 + n = 20$
6. $80 - n = 35$

TIMS Task

1. 54   2. 17
3. 53   4. 6
5. 9   6. 45

 Fact Families

Solve each pair of related facts. Then name two other facts in the same fact family.

1. $2 \times 6 =$ $12 \div 6 =$
2. $5 \times 3 =$ $3 \times 5 =$
3. $8 \times 2 =$ $16 \div 8 =$
4. $7 \times 3 =$ $3 \times 7 =$
5. $12 \div 4 =$ $4 \times 3 =$

TIMS Bit

1. 12, 2, $6 \times 2 = 12$,
   $12 \div 2 = 6$
2. 15, 15, $15 \div 5 = 3$,
   $15 \div 3 = 5$
3. 16, 2, $2 \times 8 = 16$,
   $16 \div 2 = 8$
4. 21, 21, $21 \div 3 = 7$,
   $21 \div 7 = 3$
5. 3, 12, $12 \div 3 = 4$,
   $3 \times 4 = 12$

Baseball Cards

Tim bought a notebook and a package of 65 plastic pages with pockets to hold his baseball cards. Each page had 3 rows of 3 pockets on the front side and another 3 rows of 3 pockets on the back side.

1. How many baseball cards did each page hold?

2. How many baseball cards could be held with all the pages?

TIMS Task

1. 18 cards

   $3 \times 3 = 9$ cards on the front side

   $3 \times 3 = 9$ cards on the back side

2. 1170 cards; Students will need calculators to solve this problem.

   18 cards × 65 pages = 1170 cards

Student Questions	Teacher Notes

 Working with Fact Families for × and ÷

Solve the problems below and complete the number sentences for the related facts.

A. $2 \times 7 = $ ___

___ $\div 2 = $ ___

___ $\div 7 = $ ___

___ $\times 2 = $ ___

B. $3 \times 9 = $ ___

___ $\div 9 = $ ___

___ $\div 3 = $ ___

___ $\times 3 = $ ___

C. $3 \times 6 = $ ___

___ $\div 3 = $ ___

___ $\div 6 = $ ___

___ $\times 3 = $ ___

D. $2 \times 4 = $ ___

___ $\times 2 = $ ___

___ $\div 4 = $ ___

___ $\div 2 = $ ___

E. $2 \times 9 = $ ___

___ $\div 9 = $ ___

$9 \times $ ___ $= $ ___

___ $\div 2 = $ ___

F. $8 \times 3 = $ ___

___ $\div 8 = $ ___

___ $\div 3 = $ ___

___ $\times $ ___ $= $ ___

G. $3 \times 10 = $ ___

___ $\div 3 = $ ___

$10 \times $ ___ $= $ ___

___ $\div 10 = $ ___

H. $2 \times $ ___ $= 20$

___ $\div 2 = $ ___

$20 \div 10 = $ ___

$10 \times $ ___ $= 20$

Teacher Notes

TIMS Bit

A. $2 \times 7 = 14$, $14 \div 2 = 7$, $14 \div 7 = 2$, $7 \times 2 = 14$

B. $3 \times 9 = 27$, $27 \div 9 = 3$, $27 \div 3 = 9$, $9 \times 3 = 27$

C. $3 \times 6 = 18$, $18 \div 3 = 6$, $18 \div 6 = 3$, $6 \times 3 = 18$

D. $2 \times 4 = 8$, $4 \times 2 = 8$, $8 \div 4 = 2$, $8 \div 2 = 4$

E. $2 \times 9 = 18$, $18 \div 9 = 2$, $9 \times 2 = 18$, $18 \div 2 = 9$

F. $8 \times 3 = 24$, $24 \div 8 = 3$, $24 \div 3 = 8$, $3 \times 8 = 24$,

G. $3 \times 10 = 30$, $30 \div 3 = 10$, $10 \times 3 = 30$, $30 \div 10 = 3$

H. $2 \times 10 = 20$, $20 \div 2 = 10$, $20 \div 10 = 2$, $10 \times 2 = 20$

Counting Square Units

1. How many square inches are there in one square foot? The sketch below may help you.

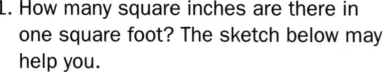

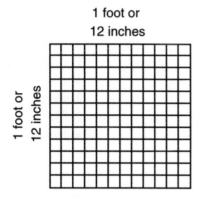

2. How many square feet are in one square yard? Draw a sketch to help you. (*Hint:* 3 feet = 1 yard)

1. 12 inches × 12 inches = 144 square inches

2. 3 feet × 3 feet = 9 square feet

 Keep on Working

Keenya helped her mother work in the garden. She worked for 2 hours and 45 minutes on Saturday and 3 hours and 30 minutes on Sunday. What was the total time she spent working in the garden?

TIMS Bit

6 hours and 15 minutes

Student Questions	Teacher Notes

J Going to the Movies

TIMS Task

1. Roberto went to the movies on Saturday with his mother, father, and his 2 younger sisters. Tickets cost $6.00 for adults and $4.50 for children. How much did it cost the family to go to the movies?

2. Prices on Tuesdays are only $4.50 for adults and $3.00 for children. How much will Roberto's family save if they go to the movies on Tuesday instead of Saturday?

1. One solution:
   $2 \times \$6.00 + 3 \times \$4.50 =$
   $\$12.00 + \$13.50 = \$25.50$

2. One way is to find the price on Tuesday and subtract:
   $2 \times \$4.50 + 3 \times \$3.00 =$
   $\$9.00 + \$9.00 = \$18.00$.
   They would have saved
   $\$25.50 - \$18.00 = \$7.50$.
   Another way is to note that the prices for both adult and children's tickets are $1.50 less on Tuesday. Since they bought 5 tickets, they would have spent $5 \times \$1.50 = \$7.50$ less on Tuesday.

K Multiples of a Number

TIMS Bit

1. Is 9 a multiple of 2? Why or why not?

2. Is 15 a multiple of 3? Why or why not?

3. Is 3 a factor of 18? Why or why not?

4. Is 2 a factor of 7? Why or why not?

5. Name three numbers greater than 21 that are multiples of 2.

6. Name three factors of 12.

1. No; Students may skip count: 2, 4, 6, 8, 10. Or, students may reason that a rectangle cannot be formed with 9 tiles using 2 tiles in each row. (Students build rectangles using square-inch tiles in Lesson 1.)

2. Yes; Students may skip count: 3, 6, 9, 12, 15. Students may say that $3 \times 5 = 15$. Others may say that a rectangle with 3 rows of 5 tiles can be formed. This rectangle would have 15 square-inch tiles.

3. Yes; $18 \div 3 = 6$; 3 evenly divides 18; 6 is a whole number.

4. No; $7 \div 2 = 3.5$; 3.5 is not a whole number.

5. Students may skip count until they reach beyond 21. Three possible answers are: 22, 24, 26.

6. Answers will vary. The factors of 12 are 1, 2, 3, 4, 6, 12.

Student Questions	Teacher Notes

 Tiling the Shower

Myrna Myrmidon and her Aunt Penny want to tile 3 walls of their shower. Each wall is 3 inches by 2 inches. How many square-inch tiles will they need in all? If the tiles come in packages of 10, how many packages should they buy?

TIMS Task

Students might think a shower 3 inches by 2 inches does not make sense. However, remind students that Myrna Myrmidon and Aunt Penny are two ants that live in Antopolis. They were introduced in Unit 2. Constructing runways for Antopolis Airport was the context for learning about area and perimeter.

Each of the three walls is 6 square inches.

Altogether, the three walls have a total area of 18 square inches.

They will need 2 boxes.

 Making Rectangles with Tiles

Make a table like the one below to show all the different rectangles that can be made with 54 tiles. You can use a calculator or multiplication facts to help you divide.

Number of Rows	Number in Each Row	Division Sentence
1	54	54 ÷ 1 = 54
2		54 ÷ 2 =

TIMS Bit

Possible rectangles are:

1 × 54, 2 × 27,

3 × 18, and 6 × 9

2	27	54 ÷ 2 = 27
3	18	54 ÷ 3 = 18
6	9	54 ÷ 6 = 9

Because of our agreement that we will consider rectangles to be the same if one can be turned to look just like the other, it is not necessary to list 9, 18, 27, and 54 rows of tiles. However, some students might prefer to make this complete list.

9	6	54 ÷ 9 = 6
18	3	54 ÷ 18 = 3
27	2	54 ÷ 27 = 2
54	1	54 ÷ 54 = 1

Making Brownies

Jenny plans to make 2 batches of brownies for her class's bake sale. There are 32 brownies in a batch.

If she puts 4 brownies in each bag and each bag sells for 50¢, how much money will her class make selling Jenny's brownies?

TIMS Task

Two batches is 64 brownies.

At 4 brownies per bag, there will be 16 bags.

If each bag sells for 50¢, the class will earn 16 × 50¢ = $8.00

Play *Digits Game*

Play *Digits Game* for addition. Draw boxes like these on your paper. As your teacher or classmate chooses the digits, write them in the boxes. Try to find the largest sum. Remember that each digit will be read only once.

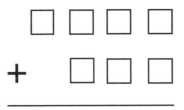

TIMS Bit

To begin the game, students draw the boxes on their papers as shown. The teacher chooses a digit at random from a set of *Digit Cards* (0–9). (*Digit Cards* can be found in the Generic Section of the *Unit Resource Guide.* As an alternative, you can use a deck of playing cards. The ace can stand for 1 and the joker or a face card can stand for zero.) Students write the digit in a box in such a way as to try to get the largest sum. Once a digit is placed, it can't be moved. Then, the teacher chooses a second digit without replacing the first. Play continues until the teacher has read enough digits to fill the boxes. The players with the largest sum win. Play again; however, change the addition sign to a subtraction sign. This time students try to find the largest difference.

Student Questions	Teacher Notes

 Addition and Subtraction

Use a paper-and-pencil method or mental math to find exact answers to these problems. Estimate to see if your answers make sense.

1. A.   4356
       − 436

    B.   5236
       +   89

    C.   4296
       + 2907

    D.   34,500
       −   4003

2. Explain your strategy for a problem you solved using mental math.

TIMS Task

1. A. 3920

   B. 5325

   C. 7203

   D. 30,497

2. A possible strategy
   for problem A:
   56 − 36 = 20 (counting by
   tens up from 36, 46, 56).
   4300 − 400 = 3900
   (counting back).
   3900 + 20 = 3920.

See the Daily Practice and Problems Guide for this unit for a discussion of a mental math strategy for Question D.

 Time Goes By

1. Nicholas arrived at his friend's house at:

His dad picked him up at:

How long was Nicholas's visit?

2. Nicholas ate dinner at:

He went to bed at:

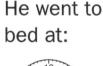

How much time passed from dinner to bedtime?

TIMS Bit

1. 3 hours and 30 minutes

2. 3 hours and 20 minutes

Student Questions	Teacher Notes

 What Numbers Are We?

TIMS Task

1. I am more than 50 and less than 60. Both my digits are the same. Who am I?

2. I am more than 2 × 45 and less than 2 × 50. If you skip count by 5s you will hit me. Who am I?

3. I am even. I am less than 3 × 6 but more than 3 × 5. Who am I?

4. Make up your own riddle. Write it down and trade with a friend. Can you solve your friend's riddle?

1. 55

2. 95

3. 16

4. Answers will vary.

 Quiz on 2s and 3s

TIMS Bit

A. 4 × 2 =   B. 3 × 2 =

C. 5 × 3 =   D. 2 × 10 =

E. 6 × 3 =   F. 2 × 5 =

G. 10 × 3 =   H. 7 × 2 =

I. 8 × 3 =   J. 3 × 3 =

K. 8 × 2 =   L. 2 × 2 =

M. 9 × 2 =   N. 6 × 2 =

O. 3 × 7 =   P. 4 × 3 =

Q. 3 × 9 =   R. 1 × 3 =

This quiz is on the second group of multiplication facts, the twos and threes. We recommend 2 minutes for this quiz. Allow students to change pens after the time is up and complete the remaining problems in a different color.

After students take the quiz, have them update their *Multiplication Facts I Know* charts.

Student Questions	Teacher Notes

 You Are Breathtaking!

Work with a partner. With a stopwatch or by watching the second hand on a clock, you and your partner will time how long each of you can hold your breath. Collect data from at least 8 students.

1. What is the median time for your data?

2. By how many seconds does your time differ from the median time?

3. Name some of the variables that may affect how long a person can hold his or her breath.

TIMS Challenge

Make sure that students take some time to practice starting, stopping, and resetting the stopwatches.

1. Students can contribute individual data to a group data table on an overhead or chalkboard in order to find the median.

2. To find the difference between the individual's time and the median, students should subtract the smaller number from the larger. Answers will vary.

3. Age, health, body size, physical fitness, etc.

Daily Practice and Problems: Bits for Lesson 1

A. Triangle Flash Cards: 2s and 3s

   (URG p. 11)

With a partner, use your *Triangle Flash Cards* to quiz each other on the multiplication facts involving twos and threes. One partner covers the shaded corner (containing the highest number). This number will be the answer to a multiplication fact called the product. The second person multiplies the two other numbers, one of which is circled and the other is in a square. These two are the factors.

Separate the used cards into three piles: those facts you know and can answer quickly, those that you can figure out with a strategy, and those that you need to learn. Practice the last two piles again and then make a list of the facts you need to practice at home for homework.

Circle the facts you know and can answer quickly on your *Multiplication Facts I Know* chart.

C. Using Twos (URG p. 12)

Do these problems in your head. Write only the answers.

A. $2 \times 9 =$ B. $3 \times 200 =$

C. $2 \times 1000 =$ D. $8 \times 2 =$

E. $5 \times 20 =$ F. $20 \times 2 =$

G. $40 \times 2 =$ H. $6 \times 2 =$

I. $2 \times 7 =$ J. $0 \times 2 =$

E. Fact Families (URG p. 13)

Solve each pair of related facts. Then name two other facts in the same fact family.

1. $2 \times 6 =$ $12 \div 6 =$

2. $5 \times 3 =$ $3 \times 5 =$

3. $8 \times 2 =$ $16 \div 8 =$

4. $7 \times 3 =$ $3 \times 7 =$

5. $12 \div 4 =$ $4 \times 3 =$

DPP Tasks are on page 29. Suggestions for using the DPPs are on pages 29–30.

LESSON GUIDE

Multiplication and Rectangles

Estimated Class Sessions: **3**

This activity has two parts. In the first part, students explore multiplication by investigating the dimensions of rectangular arrays. Student groups are assigned numbers from 1–25. For each of their numbers, they arrange that number of square-inch tiles into rectangles in as many ways as possible, then draw the rectangles on *Square-Inch Grid Paper* and cut them out. They put their rectangles on a class chart of all the numbers from 1–25.

In the second part of the activity, students use their rectangles to investigate multiples, prime numbers, composite numbers, and square numbers. The use of exponents to write square numbers is introduced.

Key Content

- Identifying prime, composite, and square numbers.
- Exploring multiplication through rectangular arrays.
- Using exponents to write square numbers.
- Finding all the factors of a number using rectangular arrays.
- Exploring fact families using rectangular arrays.

Key Vocabulary

array
commutative property of multiplication
   or turn-around rule
composite number
even number
exponent
multiple
odd number
prime number
square number

Curriculum Sequence

Before This Unit

Arrays. Students used arrays made with square-inch tiles to explore multiplication in Grade 3 Unit 11.

After This Unit

Facts. Students use multiples, factors, and square numbers to review the multiplication facts in the Daily Practice and Problems in this and succeeding units.

Exponents. Students will explore and use exponents to solve problems in this unit and in Unit 6.

Materials List

Print Materials for Students

		Math Facts and Daily Practice and Problems	Activity	Homework
Student Books	Student Guide		Multiplication and Rectangles Pages 96–99	Multiplication and Rectangles Homework Section Pages 100–101
	Discovery Assignment Book		Rectangles Page 45	Home Practice Part 1 Page 39, Triangle Flash Cards: 2s Page 41, and Triangle Flash Cards: 3s Page 43
Teacher Resources	Facts Resource Guide ⊙	DPP Items 4A, 4B, 4C, 4E & 4F Use Triangle Flash Cards: 2s and Triangle Flash Cards: 3s to review the multiplication facts for 2s and 3s.		
	Unit Resource Guide ⊙	DPP Items A–F Pages 11–13		
	Generic Section ⊙		Small Multiplication Tables, 1 per student (to tape on desk), and Square-Inch Grid Paper, 4–5 per group plus extras	

⊙ available on Teacher Resource CD

All Transparency Masters, Blackline Masters, and Assessment Blackline Masters in the Unit Resource Guide are on the Teacher Resource CD.

Supplies for Each Student Group

50 square-inch tiles per group (3–4 students)
scissors
resealable plastic bag for storing tiles, optional

tape
envelopes (for storing flash cards)

Materials for the Teacher

Observational Assessment Record (Unit Resource Guide, Pages 7–8 and Teacher Resource CD)
sheets of easel paper or construction paper for mounting rectangles on class chart, one for each
 number 1–25

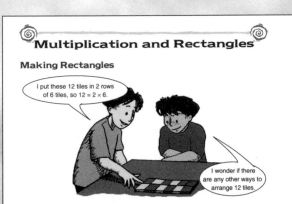

Multiplication and Rectangles

Making Rectangles

I put these 12 tiles in 2 rows of 6 tiles, so 12 = 2 × 6.

I wonder if there are any other ways to arrange 12 tiles.

1. Make as many different rectangles as you can using 12 square-inch tiles. Then, complete a table like the one below to record your rectangles.

Rectangles Possible with 12 Tiles

Number of Rows	Number in Each Row	Multiplication Sentence
2	6	2 × 6 = 12

2. Draw your rectangles on *Square-Inch Grid Paper* and cut them out. Write a multiplication number sentence on each rectangle to match. Some rectangles like the 1 × 12 and 12 × 1 rectangles shown here have the same shape when you turn them sideways. You only have to cut out one of these.

Student Guide - Page 96

Content Note

Commutative Property of Multiplication. This is a good opportunity to discuss the commutative property of multiplication, which says that the order of factors in a multiplication sentence doesn't matter. Both 3 × 4 and 4 × 3 equal 12. Changing the order of the factors merely corresponds to turning the rectangle, but it doesn't change the number of tiles it contains. In third grade, students used the term **turn-around** rule instead of **commutative property.** Either term would be appropriate here.

In order for students to appreciate the commutative property of multiplication, ask them to consider whether other operations are commutative. Addition is commutative (4 + 2 = 6 and 2 + 4 = 6). Division is not commutative: six cookies divided among three children gives two cookies per child (6 ÷ 3 = 2), but three cookies divided among six children gives only one-half cookie per child (3 ÷ 6 = $\frac{1}{2}$). Subtraction also is not commutative (5 − 2 = 3, but 2 − 5 = −3).

The commutative property has to do with the order in which things can happen. Putting on your shirt and jeans is commutative (the order in which you do it does not matter), but putting on your shoes and socks is not (the order certainly does matter).

Students might wonder why the commutative property has its name. It might help them to think of the meaning of the word "commute." Their parents might commute, or travel, to work. The commutative property of multiplication says that the factors in a multiplication sentence can travel, or change places, but their product stays the same.

Before the Activity

Make copies of the *Small Multiplication Tables* Generic Page and cut out the tables. Give each student a table to tape to his or her desk. Students can refer to the tables as they work on this and future activities. In this way, students practice using the facts in many problem-solving situations and develop confidence that they have the tools they need to find solutions.

Count out 50 tiles per group of three to four students in advance and place them in resealable bags to make distribution easier.

> **TIMS Tip**
>
> During multiplication fact quizzes, students can cover the tables with a book.

Developing the Activity

Part 1. Making Rectangles

Questions 1–6 on the *Multiplication and Rectangles* Activity Pages in the *Student Guide* provide a summary of the steps described in this section. You may prefer, however, to introduce the activity without the activity pages.

Introducing the Activity with 12 and 18 Tiles.

Distribute 50 tiles to each group of three to four students. *Question 1* asks students to make a rectangle using 12 square-inch tiles. Ask:

- *What is the area of the rectangles you made?* (12 square inches, regardless of the shape)
- *How many rows are in your rectangle?*
- *How many tiles are in each row?*
- *How many different rectangles did the class make?*

The class will need to agree on what it means for two rectangles to be different. For example, should they consider a 3 × 4 rectangle, which has three rows and four columns different from or the same as a 4 × 3 rectangle, which has four rows and three columns. Tell them that later in the activity *(Question 2),* they will draw their rectangles on paper and cut them out. If the cutout rectangles are turned, it will not be possible to tell the 3 × 4 rectangle apart from the 4 × 3 rectangle. Therefore, for this activity, rectangles will be considered the same if one can be turned to look just like the other. With this convention, there are three different rectangles that can be made with 12 tiles: 1 × 12, 2 × 6, and 3 × 4.

After discussing the different rectangles that can be made with an area of 12 square inches, ask students to draw all three rectangles on *Square-Inch Grid Paper* and cut them out. (Have tape available so they can tape pieces together to make the long, skinny rectangle.) Then, have them write an appropriate multiplication sentence on each rectangle, as shown in Figure 3.

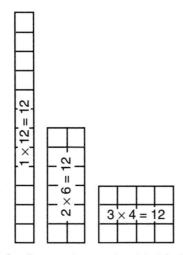

Figure 3: *Rectangles made with 12 tiles*

Question 3 asks students to investigate the rectangles that can be made using 18 tiles. They should make all the possible rectangles (there are three), trace the rectangles onto *Square-Inch Grid Paper,* cut them out, and write appropriate number sentences. Discuss their results. Ask how they can be sure they found all the possible rectangles. Suggest systematically checking each possibility. Can they put 1 tile in each row? 2 in each row? 3 in each row? 4 in each row? etc. Remind students that they need to make only one rectangle for each pair of factors such as 3×6 and 6×3.

Making a Class Chart of Rectangles with 1 to 25 Tiles. After students have investigated the rectangles for 12 and 18 tiles, assign the numbers from 1–25 to different groups. Working together, groups will use tiles to make all possible rectangles for their numbers, then draw the rectangles on *Square-Inch Grid Paper* and cut them out as described in *Question 4.* They will write multiplication sentences on their rectangles and finally, they will mount their rectangles on a class chart (*Question 5*) as shown in Figure 5.

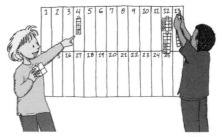

3. Find all the rectangles you can make with 18 tiles. Follow the directions from Questions 1 and 2 using 18 tiles.

4. Your teacher will assign your group some of the numbers from 1 to 25.
   - For each number, arrange that many tiles into rectangles in as many ways as you can.
   - Then, draw the rectangles on *Square-Inch Grid Paper* and cut them out. Write number sentences on each rectangle to match.

5. Put your rectangles on a class chart.

6. Use the class chart of rectangles to make a table, like the one at the right, of the multiplication sentences for each of the numbers from 1–25. Use the *Rectangles* Activity Page in the *Discovery Assignment Book.*

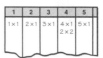

Multiples

Use the rectangles the class made to answer the following questions:

7. Which numbers have rectangles with 2 rows? List them from smallest to largest.

8. Which numbers have rectangles with 3 rows? List them from smallest to largest.

Multiplication and Rectangles   SG · Grade 4 · Unit 4 · Lesson 1   97

Student Guide - Page 97

Assign numbers to the groups so that the more interesting numbers listed below are distributed evenly among the groups.

prime numbers: 1, 2, 3, 5, 7, 11, 13, 17, 19, 23
odd numbers that are not prime: 9, 15, 21, 25
numbers with 3 or more rectangles: 12 (done in class), 16, 18 (done in class), 20, 24
square numbers 4, 9 (listed above), 16 (listed above), 25 (listed above)

Assign each group some numbers to post and some to check (these will be posted by other groups). For example, if you are working with 8 groups, you might use the following distribution of numbers.

Group	Numbers to Post	Numbers to Check
Group 1	1, 16, 23	2, 9, 22
Group 2	2, 9, 22, 12 (done in class)	1, 7, 16, 23
Group 3	3, 10, 25	6, 13, 16
Group 4	4, 13, 21	3, 15, 20
Group 5	5, 15, 20	8, 11, 14, 25
Group 6	6, 11, 18 (done in class)	5, 9, 10, 20
Group 7	7, 19, 24	4, 17, 21
Group 8	8, 14, 17	19, 24, 25

Figure 4: *Number distribution*

Encourage students to speculate in advance about the rectangles that are possible. One common prediction is that the odd numbers will have only one rectangle each. Students will probably revise their thinking when they build rectangles with 9, 15, 21, or 25 tiles.

Ask students to post their rectangles on a class chart. Make a large chart on easel paper, putting columns for each number. See Figure 5. Alternatively, use separate sheets of construction paper, with a number written on top of each, and post the sheets (in order) around the room.

Ask students to complete the table on the *Rectangles* Activity Page in the *Discovery Assignment Book,* as shown in Figure 6 (***Question 6*** in the *Student Guide*). Completing this table will help students make a connection between the rectangles and multiplication.

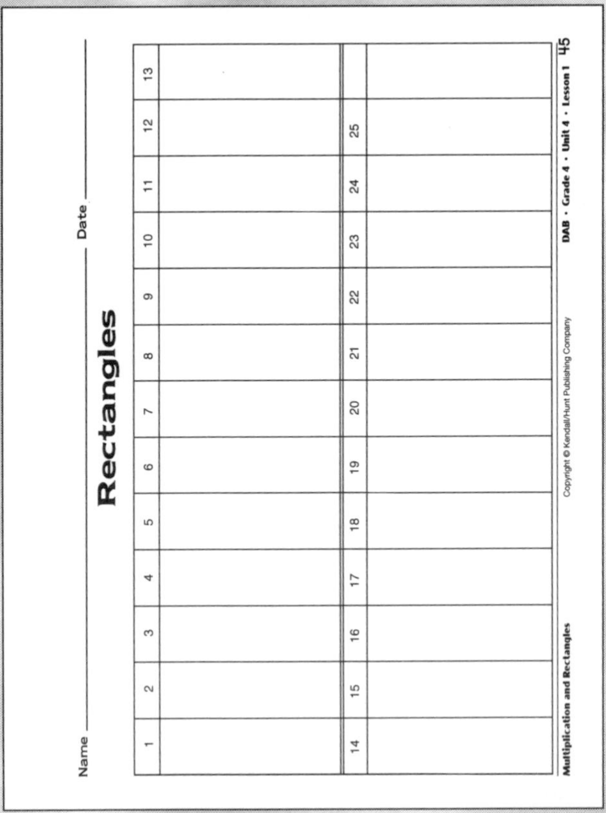
Name ______ Date ______

Rectangles

1	2	3	4	5	6	7	8	9	10	11	12	13

14	15	16	17	18	19	20	21	22	23	24	25

Multiplication and Rectangles

DAB · Grade 4 · Unit 4 · Lesson 1 45

***Discovery Assignment Book* - Page 45**

Figure 5: *Students making class chart of rectangles made with 1–25 tiles*

TIMS Tip

Keep this chart up for several days if possible. Students will need to refer to it in some of the lessons that follow.

1	2	3	4	5	6	7	8	9	10	11	12	13
1 × 1	2 × 1	3 × 1	4 × 1 2 × 2	5 × 1	6 × 1 3 × 2	7 × 1	8 × 1 4 × 2	9 × 1 3 × 3	10 × 1 2 × 5	11 × 1	12 × 1 6 × 2 3 × 4	13 × 1

14	15	16	17	18	19	20	21	22	23	24	25	
14 × 1 2 × 7	15 × 1 3 × 5	16 × 1 4 × 4 8 × 2	17 × 1	18 × 1 9 × 2 6 × 3	19 × 1	20 × 1 4 × 5 2 × 10	21 × 1 7 × 3	22 × 1 11 × 2	23 × 1	24 × 1 12 × 2 8 × 3 6 × 4	25 × 1 5 × 5	

Figure 6: Rectangles *Activity Page with answers*

A number is a **multiple** of 2 if it equals 2 times another whole number. If you can make a rectangle with 2 rows for a number then it is a multiple of 2.

Numbers that are multiples of two (2, 4, 6, 8, etc.) are called **even numbers.** Numbers that are not multiples of 2 (1, 3, 5, 7, etc.) are called **odd numbers.**

When you skip count, you say the multiples of a number. For example, skip counting by 3 gives the multiples of 3. The multiples of 3 are 3, 6, 9, 12, and so on. They are all the numbers that have rectangles with 3 rows.

9. Which numbers on the chart are multiples of 4 (have a rectangle with 4 rows)? List them from smallest to largest.

10. Which numbers on the chart are multiples of 5? List them from smallest to largest.

Prime Numbers

11. A. How many different rectangles can you make with 5 tiles?
    B. How many with 7 tiles?

Numbers that are larger than one and have only one rectangle have a special name. They are called **prime numbers.** For example, 5 and 7 are prime numbers.

12. List the prime numbers between 1 and 25.

13. Are all odd numbers prime? Explain.

Square Numbers

The number nine is special because it has a rectangle that is a square that has three rows and three columns.

14. Which other numbers have rectangles that are squares? These numbers are called **square numbers.**

15. Find the next largest square number after 25.

16. Another way mathematicians write 3×3 is 3^2. This is read "three to the second power" or "three squared." The raised 2 is called an **exponent.** Here are some more examples:

$$1^2 = 1 \times 1 = 1$$
$$2^2 = 2 \times 2 = 4$$
$$3^2 = 3 \times 3 = 9$$
$$4^2 = 4 \times 4 = 16$$

A. What is 5^2?
B. What is 6^2?

98   SG · Grade 4 · Unit 4 · Lesson 1   **Multiplication and Rectangles**

Student Guide - Page 98

Arrays and Fact Families

17. My rectangle has a total of 18 square tiles. It has 3 rows of tiles.
    A. How many tiles are in each row? Write a number sentence for this rectangle.
    B. What are the other three sentences that are in this same family? Explain how all these sentences fit with this rectangle. Use the total number in each column in your explanation.

18. Another rectangle has 3 rows of tiles and a total of 24 square tiles.
    A. Write a number sentence to fit this rectangle.
    B. What are all the other number sentences in the same fact family?

19. A. Write a multiplication number sentence for a rectangle with 4 tiles in all and 2 tiles in each row.
    B. Can you write a different multiplication sentence for this rectangle? Why or why not?
    C. Write a division sentence for this rectangle.
    D. Can you write a different division sentence for this number?

20. A rectangle is made of 9 tiles and has 3 tiles in each row.
    A. How many different number sentences can you write for this rectangle?
    B. Look at the rectangles for the other square numbers. How many facts are in their fact families?

21. A. Write all the number sentences in the fact family for 5×2.
    B. Write all the number sentences in the fact family for 5^2.

Multiplication and Rectangles   SG · Grade 4 · Unit 4 · Lesson 1   99

Student Guide - Page 99

Part 2. Multiplies, Primes, and Square Numbers

After the class chart is completed, ask students to work on the problems in the sections Multiples, Prime Numbers, Square Numbers, and Arrays and Fact Families on the *Multiplication and Rectangles* Activity Pages in the *Student Guide.*

Multiples are defined operationally. A number is a **multiple** of 2, for example, if it can be made into a rectangle with 2 rows. Also, multiples of a number are the numbers you say when you skip count by that number. *(Questions 7–10)*

Prime numbers are defined as numbers that are larger than one and have only one rectangle. *(Questions 11–13)* We will return to prime numbers in the next lesson and define them in terms of their factors.

Content Note

One Is Not Prime. Since a **prime number** is conventionally taken to be a number with exactly two factors (itself and one), one is not considered to be prime. Note that two is prime since its only factors are itself and one. Two is the only even prime number.

Composite Numbers. During the discussion of prime numbers, the question sometimes arises of what to call numbers that are not prime numbers, the ones that have more than one rectangular array. Tell students that these are called composite numbers. The definition of a composite number is one that has more than two distinct factors. All numbers that are not prime numbers and are not one (1) are composite numbers.

A nice feature of this activity is that students will see clearly why the **square numbers** have their names. *(Questions 14–16)* Exponents are introduced as a way to write square numbers: $5 \times 5 = 5^2$. We will return to exponents in Lesson 3.

Questions 17–18 lead students to connect this lesson to their work with fact families in Unit 3. If a number sentence matches a rectangle, then all the number sentences in that fact family also match the same rectangle. Have students explain how the rectangle can be used to illustrate all four members of the fact family. Demonstrate on the overhead projector by turning a transparency of a rectangle to show the different facts represented.

$3 \times 6 = 18$ and $18 \div 3 = 6$

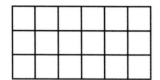

$6 \times 3 = 18$ and $18 \div 6 = 3$

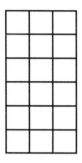

Questions 19–20 investigate fact families for square numbers. These fact families only have two number sentences since there is only one multiplication sentence and one division. For example, "turning around" the factors in the sentence $2 \times 2 = 4$ produces the same number sentence. *Question 21* calls attention to the difference between 5×2 and 5^2. Students write fact families for $5 \times 2 = 10$ and 5^2 ($5 \times 5 = 25$).

Suggestions for Teaching the Lesson

Math Facts

DPP Bit A and Home Practice Part 1 begin the use of *Triangle Flash Cards* to practice the twos and threes multiplication facts. For Task B students find patterns using math facts. Students practice the facts for the twos and threes using multiples of ten in Bit C. Bit E provides practice with fact families. Task F is a word problem that uses multiplication facts for the threes.

Daily Practice and Problems: Tasks for Lesson 1

B. Task: Pattern Triangle (URG p. 12)

Look at the triangle and answer the following questions.

1. Describe any patterns in the rows (across).

2. Do the diagonal columns show any patterns?

3. Complete the last row of the triangle.

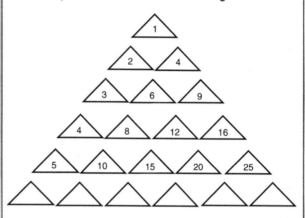

D. Task: What's Missing? (URG p. 13)

The letter *n* stands for a missing number. What number must *n* be to make each number sentence true?

1. $30 + 24 = n$ 2. $n - 8 = 9$

3. $n - 20 = 33$ 4. $15 + n = 21$

5. $11 + n = 20$ 6. $80 - n = 35$

F. Task: Baseball Cards (URG p. 13)

Tim bought a notebook and a package of 65 plastic pages with pockets to hold his baseball cards. Each page had 3 rows of 3 pockets on the front side and another 3 rows of 3 pockets on the back side.

1. How many baseball cards did each page hold?

2. How many baseball cards could be held with all the pages?

Discovery Assignment Book - Page 39

Name _____ Date _____

Unit 4: Home Practice

Part 1 Triangle Flash Cards: 2s and 3s

Study for the quiz on the multiplication facts for the 2s and 3s. Take home your *Triangle Flash Cards: 2s and 3s* and your list of facts you need to study.

Here's how to use the flash cards. Ask a family member to choose one flash card at a time. He or she should cover the corner containing the highest number. This number will be the answer to a multiplication fact. Multiply the two uncovered numbers.

Study the math facts in small groups. Choose to study 8 to 10 facts each night. Your teacher will tell you when the quiz on the 2s and 3s will be.

Part 2 Multiplication: Factors, Multiples, Primes, and Squares

To solve the following problems, you may use your *Student Guide* as a reference. See Unit 4 Lessons 1, 2, and 4.

1. Is 34 a multiple of 2? Explain why or why not.

2. Is 3 a factor of 35? Explain why or why not.

3. Name 10 numbers that are multiples of 2.

4. Name 10 numbers that have 3 as a factor.

5. Is 7 a prime number? Why or why not?

6. A. $5^2 =$ B. $10^2 =$
    C. $2^2 =$ D. $3^2 =$

PRODUCTS AND FACTORS   DAB · Grade 4 · Unit 4   39

Copyright © Kendall/Hunt Publishing Company

Suggestions for Teaching the Lesson (continued)

Homework and Practice

- Assign *Questions 1–10* in the Homework section on the *Multiplication and Rectangles* Activity Pages in the *Student Guide*. It may help some students to have a sheet of *Square-Inch Grid Paper* so that they can easily draw rectangles as they do their homework. Use one or two examples from *Question 1* to demonstrate how to solve a problem by drawing rectangles.

- DPP Task D provides practice finding an unknown in a number sentence.

- Home Practice Part 1 reminds students to practice multiplication facts for the twos and threes using their *Triangle Flash Cards*.

Student Guide - Page 100

Homework

You can draw pictures of rectangles on *Square-Inch Grid Paper* to help you solve these problems.

1. John built rectangles with 20 tiles, but some of his work was erased. Help John fill in the missing numbers.

Rectangles Possible with 20 Tiles

Number of Rows	Number in Each Row	Multiplication Sentence
1		$1 \times ? = 20$
	10	$? \times 10 = 20$
4		$4 \times ? = 20$
5		$5 \times ? = 20$
	2	$? \times 2 = 20$
20		$20 \times ? = 20$

2. A. Is 36 an even number? How do you know?
   B. Is 36 a square number? How do you know?

3. Find multiples by skip counting.
   A. Multiples of 2: Start at zero and skip count by 2s to 50.
   B. Multiples of 3: Start at zero and skip count by 3s to 48.
   C. Multiples of 5: Start at zero and skip count by 5s to 50.
   D. Multiples of 6: Start at zero and skip count by 6s to 48.

4. Tell whether the following numbers are even or odd.
   A. 10   B. 17   C. 21   D. 44

5. Jane says that any number that ends in 2, like 12, 72, and 102, is an even number. What other digits can even numbers end in?

100 SG · Grade 4 · Unit 4 · Lesson 1   Multiplication and Rectangles

---

Student Guide - Page 101

6. A. Which of the following are multiples of 5?
   20   34   45   56   60   73   35
   B. Can you tell whether a number is a multiple of 5 by looking at the last digit? If so, tell what digits the multiples of 5 end in.

7. A. Which number in each of the following pairs is a multiple of 3?

   11   21 (last digit 1)
   12   22 (last digit 2)
   23   33 (last digit 3)
   14   24 (last digit 4)
   15   25 (last digit 5)
   16   36 (last digit 6)
   17   27 (last digit 7)
   18   28 (last digit 8)
   39   19 (last digit 9)

   B. Can you tell whether a number is a multiple of 3 by looking at its last digit? If so, tell what digits multiples of 3 end in.

8. Write the following multiplication problems using exponents. Then multiply.
   A. 2×2 B. 5×5 C. 7×7 D. 10×10

9. Rewrite the following without using exponents. Then multiply.
   A. 8^2 B. 3^2 C. 9^2

10. Ming has 32 rocks in his rock collection. He wants to buy a rectangular display box with one square compartment for each rock. At the store he found boxes with 6 rows and 6 columns, 8 rows and 4 columns, 2 rows and 16 columns, and 3 rows and 10 columns. Which boxes will hold his collection with no empty compartments?

Multiplication and Rectangles   SG · Grade 4 · Unit 4 · Lesson 1   101

Assessment

Use the *Observational Assessment Record* to record students' abilities to represent multiplication and division problems with arrays.

Extension

Have students make an additional class chart with rectangles for prime numbers and another with rectangles for square numbers.

Literature Connection

* Hulme, Joy N. *Sea Squares.* Illustrated by Carol Schwartz. Hyperion Books for Children, New York, 1993.

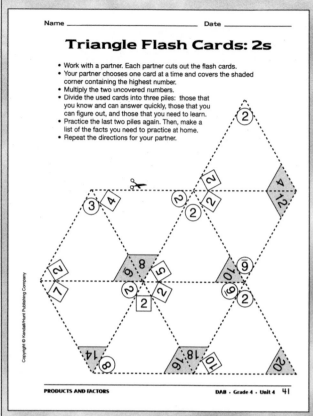

Discovery Assignment Book - Page 41

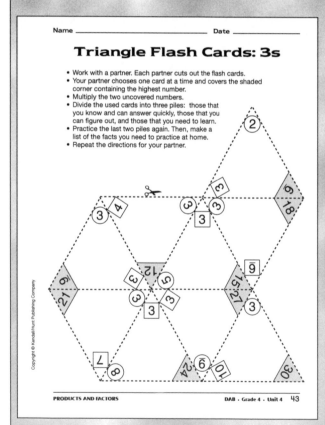

Discovery Assignment Book - Page 43

AT A GLANCE

Math Facts and Daily Practice and Problems

DPP items A–C and E–F provide practice with math facts for 2s and 3s. Task D provides computation practice using unknowns.

Part 1. Making Rectangles

1. Distribute 50 tiles to each group of three to four students.
2. Students make a rectangle using 12 square-inch tiles. Discuss the different rectangles made.
3. For each of the rectangles that can be built with 12 tiles (1×12, 2×6, and 3×4), students draw the rectangle onto *Square-Inch Grid Paper,* cut it out, and write a corresponding multiplication sentence on it.
4. Students find, draw, and cut out rectangles for 18 tiles. The class discusses the results.
5. Assign the numbers from 1–25 to different groups. Students find, draw, and cut out rectangles for each of their numbers.
6. Students post their rectangles on a class chart for the numbers 1–25. The chart is kept posted for reference throughout the unit.
7. Students complete the table on the *Rectangles* Activity Page in the *Discovery Assignment Book.*

Part 2. Multiples, Primes, and Square Numbers

Students answer and discuss *Questions 7–21* in the *Multiplication and Rectangles* Activity Pages in the *Student Guide.*

Homework

1. Assign *Questions 1–10* in the Homework section on the *Multiplication and Rectangles* Activity Pages.
2. Assign Part 1 of the Home Practice.

Assessment

Use the *Observational Assessment Record* to document students' abilities to represent multiplication and division using arrays.

Notes:

Student Guide

Questions 1–21 (SG pp. 96–99)

1. * Rectangles Possible with 12 Tiles

Number of Rows	Number in Each Row	Multiplication Sentence
2	6	$2 \times 6 = 12$
1	12	$1 \times 12 = 12$
3	4	$3 \times 4 = 12$

2.

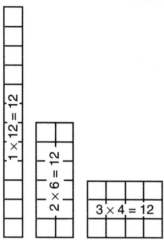

$1 \times 12 = 12$

$2 \times 6 = 12$

$3 \times 4 = 12$

3. * Rectangles Possible with 18 Tiles

Number of Rows	Number in Each Row	Multiplication Sentence
1	18	$1 \times 18 = 18$
2	9	$2 \times 9 = 18$
3	6	$3 \times 6 = 18$

4.–6. *See Figure 6 in Lesson Guide 1 for possible rectangles for each number from 1−25.

7. 2, 4, 6, 8, 10, 12, 14, 16, 18, 20, 22, 24

8. 3, 6, 9, 12, 15, 18, 21, 24

9. 4, 8, 12, 16, 20, 24

10. 5, 10, 15, 20, 25

11. **A.** Only 1 rectangle: 1×5 rectangle (5×1 rectangle is the same.)

    B. Only 1 rectangle: 1×7 rectangle (7×1 rectangle is the same.)

12. 2, 3, 5, 7, 11, 13, 17, 19, and 23

13. No, the numbers 9 and 15 are odd, but they are not prime numbers.

14. 4, 16, and 25

15. 36 ($6 \times 6 = 36$)

16. **A.** $5 \times 5 = 25$

    B. $6 \times 6 = 36$

17. **A.** 6, $3 \times 6 = 18$

    B. $6 \times 3 = 18$: 6 tiles in a row times 3 rows equals 18 total tiles

    $18 \div 3 = 6$: 18 total tiles divided into 3 rows equals 6 tiles in each row

    $18 \div 6 = 3$: 18 total tiles divided 6 tiles into each row equals 3 rows.

18. **A.** $3 \times 8 = 24$

    B. $8 \times 3 = 24$; $24 \div 3 = 8$; $24 \div 8 = 3$

19. **A.** $2 \times 2 = 4$

    B. No, because using the turn-around rule makes the same sentence.

    C. $4 \div 2 = 2$

    D. No.

20. **A.** 2 number sentences

    B. 2 facts in each fact family

21. **A.** $5 \times 2 = 10$; $2 \times 5 = 10$; $10 \div 5 = 2$; $10 \div 2 = 5$

    B. $5 \times 5 = 25$; $25 \div 5 = 5$

*Answers and/or discussion are included in the Lesson Guide.

**Answers for all the Home Practice in the *Discovery Assignment Book* are at the end of the unit.

Homework

Questions 1–10 (SG pp. 100–101)

1.   Rectangles Possible with 20 Tiles

Number of Rows	Number in Each Row	Multiplication Sentence
1	20	$1 \times 20 = 20$
2	10	$2 \times 10 = 20$
4	5	$4 \times 5 = 20$
5	4	$5 \times 4 = 20$
10	2	$10 \times 2 = 20$
20	1	$20 \times 1 = 20$

2. **A.** Yes; Explanations will vary. 36 is a multiple of 2. A rectangle with 2 rows can be made with 36 tiles.

   B. Yes; Explanations will vary. $6 \times 6 = 36$; A square can be made with 36 tiles—6 rows of 6 tiles each.

3. **A.** 0, 2, 4, 6, 8, 10, 12, 14, 16, 18, etc., to 50

   B. 0, 3, 6, 9, 12, 15, 18, 21, 24, 27, etc., to 48

   C. 0, 5, 10, 15, 20, 25, 30, etc., to 50

   D. 0, 6, 12, 18, 24, 30, 36, etc., to 48

4. **A.** even

   B. odd

   C. odd

   D. even

5. 0, 4, 6, or 8

6. **A.** 20, 45, 60, and 35

   B. Yes; 0 or 5

7. **A.** 21, 12, 33, 24, 15, 36, 27, 18, 39

   B. No

8. **A.** $2^2 = 4$

   B. $5^2 = 25$

   C. $7^2 = 49$

   D. $10^2 = 100$

9. **A.** $8 \times 8 = 64$

   B. $3 \times 3 = 9$

   C. $9 \times 9 = 81$

10. 8 rows and 4 columns; 2 rows and 16 columns

Discovery Assignment Book

Rectangles (DAB p. 45)

*See Figure 6 in Lesson Guide 1 for a completed table.

---

*Answers and/or discussion are included in the Lesson Guide.

**Answers for all the Home Practice in the *Discovery Assignment Book* are at the end of the unit.

LESSON GUIDE

Factors

Students use rectangular arrays to discuss factors, including a way to find factors using a calculator. Students find factors of several numbers and investigate prime numbers.

Key Content

- Identifying prime numbers.
- Finding factors using rectangular arrays and calculators.

Key Vocabulary

factor

Daily Practice and Problems: Bits for Lesson 2

G. Working with Fact Families for × and ÷ (URG p. 14)

Solve the problems below and complete the number sentences for the related facts.

A. $2 \times 7 =$ __
    __ $\div 2 =$ __
    __ $\div 7 =$ __
    __ $\times 2 =$ __

B. $3 \times 9 =$ __
    __ $\div 9 =$ __
    __ $\div 3 =$ __
    __ $\times 3 =$ __

C. $3 \times 6 =$ __
    __ $\div 3 =$ __
    __ $\div 6 =$ __
    __ $\times 3 =$ __

D. $2 \times 4 =$ __
    __ $\times 2 =$ __
    __ $\div 4 =$ __
    __ $\div 2 =$ __

E. $2 \times 9 =$ __
    __ $\div 9 =$ __
    $9 \times$ __ $=$ __
    __ $\div 2 =$ __

F. $8 \times 3 =$ __
    __ $\div 8 =$ __
    __ $\div 3 =$ __
    __ $\times$ __ $=$ __

G. $3 \times 10 =$ __
    __ $\div 3 =$ __
    $10 \times$ __ $=$ __
    __ $\div 10 =$ __

H. $2 \times$ __ $= 20$
    __ $\div 2 =$ __
    $20 \div 10 =$ __
    $10 \times$ __ $= 20$

I. Keep on Working (URG p. 15)

Keenya helped her mother work in the garden. She worked for 2 hours and 45 minutes on Saturday and 3 hours and 30 minutes on Sunday. What was the total time she spent working in the garden?

DPP Tasks are on page 41. Suggestions for using the DPPs are on page 41.

Curriculum Sequence

Before This Unit

Factors. In Grade 3 Unit 11, the term factor was explored using rectangles made with square-inch tiles.

After This Unit

Divisibility Rules. In Grade 4 Unit 7, students explore divisibility rules.

Materials List

Print Materials for Students

	Math Facts and Daily Practice and Problems	Activity	Homework
Student Book — Student Guide		*Factors* Pages 102–104	*Factors* Homework Section Pages 105–106
Teacher Resources — Facts Resource Guide	DPP Items 4G & 4J		
Teacher Resources — Unit Resource Guide	DPP Items G–J Pages 14–16		
Teacher Resources — Generic Section		*Small Multiplication Tables,* 1 per student (to tape on desk), *Three-column Data Table* 2 per student (optional), and *Square-Inch Grid Paper,* 3–4 per student	

available on Teacher Resource CD

All Transparency Masters, Blackline Masters, and Assessment Blackline Masters in the Unit Resource Guide are on the Teacher Resource CD.

Supplies for Each Student Group

50 square-inch tiles per group (3–4 students)
calculators

Materials for the Teacher

Observational Assessment Record (Unit Resource Guide, Pages 7–8 and Teacher Resource CD)
completed rectangles class chart from *Multiplication and Rectangles* (Lesson 1)

Developing the Activity

Part 1. Tile Problems

Ask students to complete the Tile Problems section
on the *Factors* Activity Pages in the *Student Guide.*
These problems explore the relationship between the
number of rows, the number in each row, and the
total number of tiles in the rectangles. The problems
involve multiplication and division. Students should
have square-inch tiles or a piece of *Square-Inch Grid
Paper* available to help them. Similar problems can
be found in the More Tile Problems part of the
Homework section on the *Factors* Activity Pages.
Square-Inch Grid Paper should be sent home with
these problems.

Part 2. Finding Factors

Before asking students to read the Finding Factors
section on the *Factors* Activity Pages, introduce the
topic of factors by asking the class the following
questions:

- *Can you arrange ten tiles into two equal rows?
  How can you answer this without using tiles?
  How many tiles will be in each row?* (Ask students to suggest what operation can be used to
  answer this question. Because of their work with
  fact families and rectangular arrays, students
  may suggest either a multiplication sentence,
  $2 \times ? = 10$, or a division sentence, $10 \div 2 = ?$
  They should understand that either sentence
  describes the problem accurately and fully.
  When they express the question using a division
  sentence, they can use a calculator to help
  them solve it.)

- *Can you arrange nine tiles into two equal rows?
  Give a division sentence to explain your answer.*
  (There would be $9 \div 2 = 4\frac{1}{2}$ tiles in each row.
  That is not possible unless you cut the tiles,
  which is not allowed here.)

Tell students that a number is a **factor** of another
number if it divides evenly into the number, that is,
if the answer is a whole number. Factors can also
be described as the whole numbers that can be multiplied to get the number. The answers to the above
questions show that 2 is a factor of 10, but not of 9.

Ask students to check the above questions with
their calculators. For the first question, they will
get $10 \div 2 = 5$. 2 and 5 are both factors of 10
because they divide evenly into 10 and they are two
whole numbers multiplied together to get 10.

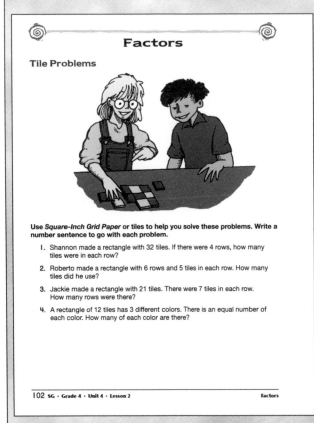

Factors

Tile Problems

Use *Square-Inch Grid Paper* or tiles to help you solve these problems. Write a
number sentence to go with each problem.

1. Shannon made a rectangle with 32 tiles. If there were 4 rows, how many
   tiles were in each row?

2. Roberto made a rectangle with 6 rows and 5 tiles in each row. How many
   tiles did he use?

3. Jackie made a rectangle with 21 tiles. There were 7 tiles in each row.
   How many rows were there?

4. A rectangle of 12 tiles has 3 different colors. There is an equal number of
   each color. How many of each color are there?

102 SG · Grade 4 · Unit 4 · Lesson 2   Factors

***Student Guide* - Page 102**

For the second question, they will get $9 \div 2 = 4.5$. This is not a whole number so 2 is not a factor of 9. Have students use their calculators to answer the following:

- *Can 51 tiles be divided evenly into 3 rows? What is the number sentence?* (Yes, $51 \div 3 = 17$ or $3 \times 17 = 51$. 3 divides 51 evenly and 3 and 17 are two whole numbers that equal 51 when multiplied together. So 3 is a factor of 51 as is 17.)

- *Can 44 tiles be divided evenly into 8 rows? What is the number sentence?* (No, $44 \div 8 = 5.5$. 8 does not divide 44 evenly, since 5.5 is not a whole number. 8 is not a factor of 44.)

- *Can 156 tiles be divided evenly into 9 rows? What is the number sentence?* (No, $156 \div 9 = 17.33333\ldots$ 9 does not divide 156 evenly, since $17.33333\ldots$ is not a whole number. 9 is not a factor of 156.)

- *Can 153 tiles be divided evenly into 9 rows? What is the number sentence?* (Yes, $153 \div 9 = 17$, $9 \times 17 = 153$. 9 divides 153 evenly. 9 and 17 are two whole numbers that equal 153 when multiplied together, so 9 is a factor of 153.)

Draw the chart shown in Figure 7 on the board. Ask the class to help you fill it in to make a list of all the rectangles that can be made with 24 tiles. They can refer to the rectangles class chart they made in Lesson 1. The chart in Figure 7 is a little different from the one made in the last lesson. Here, students write division sentences instead of multiplication sentences. Using division to look for factors is helpful, particularly when using calculators.

Rectangles Possible with 24 Tiles

Number of Rows	Number in Each Row	Division Sentence
1	24	$24 \div 1 = 24$
2	12	$24 \div 2 = 12$
3	8	$24 \div 3 = 8$
4	6	$24 \div 4 = 6$
6	4	$24 \div 6 = 4$
8	3	$24 \div 8 = 3$
12	2	$24 \div 12 = 2$
24	1	$24 \div 24 = 1$

Figure 7: *Rectangles that can be made with 24 tiles*

TIMS Tip

There are two types of division sentences possible here. If the total number of tiles is known, and the number of rows is given, then the number in each row can be found. The first type is represented by the division sentences shown in the table (24 ÷ number of rows = number in each row). If students write division sentences representing the second type (24 ÷ number in each row = number of rows), they would also be correct.

From this chart, students can find that the factors of 24 are 1, 2, 3, 4, 6, 8, 12, and 24. Note: Because of our agreement that we will consider rectangles to be the same if one can be turned to look just like the other, it is not necessary to list rows with 6, 8, 12, and 24 tiles in the table. However, some students might prefer to make this complete list.

If students need more whole-group practice, ask them to make a similar chart for the rectangles made with 28 tiles.

After finding factors as a class, read together the definition of factor in the Finding Factors section of the *Factors* Activity Pages. Then, ask students to do *Questions 5–12.* These problems include questions about factors and prime numbers. In *Questions 9–10,* students make a table similar to the one in Figure 7 to help them find the factors of 20 and 36, respectively. They can use a *Three-column Data Table* for this.

Question 9C asks students to compare their table to the table in Homework *Question 1* of Lesson 1. Here, again, the tables are the same except that in the third column, one gives multiplication sentences and the other gives the corresponding division sentences.

Prime numbers are defined prior to *Question 12.* Refer students back to Lesson 1 which defined prime numbers as numbers that are larger than one and have only one rectangle. Write the two definitions on the blackboard and have the students compare them. Ask them to reflect on how there can be two different definitions. Ask:

- *Is one definition right and one wrong?* (No, one uses the rectangular array to describe a prime number and one uses the term "factor.")

- *What is the same in the two definitions?* (A prime number is a number greater than one.)

- *What is different?* (The first says a prime number has only one rectangle; the second says a prime number has only two factors.)

- *Could it be that these two definitions say the same thing? How?* (Yes, in the rectangular array, the number of rows and the number in each row are the two factors. If there is only one rectangle that can be made, that means that there can be only two factors, one and the number itself.)

Finding Factors

Jacob wondered whether he could arrange 24 tiles into 5 rows. He used his calculator to divide 24 into 5 groups.

Hmm. 24 ÷ 5 equals 4.8, so that means 4⅘ tiles would go in each row. That's not possible, since I can't cut the tiles.

The **factors** of a number are the whole numbers that can be multiplied to get the number. For example, 3 × 8 = 24, so 3 and 8 are factors of 24. All the factors of 24 are 1, 2, 3, 4, 6, 8, 12, and 24, because we can multiply pairs of numbers to get 24 in the following ways: 1 × 24, 2 × 12, 3 × 8, and 4 × 6.

The factors of a number can also be described as the whole numbers that divide the number evenly. Two is a factor of 24 because 24 ÷ 2 = 12. But 5 is not a factor of 24 because 24 ÷ 5 = 4.8 which is not a whole number.

The factors of a number tell us which numbers of rows are possible in rectangles made with that number of tiles. Jacob couldn't make a rectangle with 5 rows and 24 tiles because 5 is not a factor of 24.

5. A. Is it possible to make a rectangle with 24 tiles and 6 rows? If so, how many tiles would be in each row? Use your calculator to check.
   B. Is it possible to make a rectangle with 24 tiles and 7 rows? Use your calculator to check. Explain.

6. A. Is 5 a factor of 38? Why or why not?
   B. Is it a factor of 35? Why or why not?

7. A. Is 8 a factor of 32? Why or why not?
   B. Is it a factor of 36? Why or why not?

Factors   SG · Grade 4 · Unit 4 · Lesson 2 103

Student Guide - Page 103

---

8. The band leader at Coleman School wants to arrange the 48 members of its marching band into rows with an equal number of students in each row.
   A. Can he arrange them into 6 rows? Is 6 a factor of 48?
   B. Can he arrange them into 7 rows? Is 7 a factor of 48?
   C. Can he arrange them into 8 rows? Is 8 a factor of 48?

9. A. Make a table like the one at right to show all of the rectangles that can be made with 20 tiles. Use a calculator or multiplication facts to help you divide.

Rectangles Possible with 20 Tiles

Number of Rows	Number in Each Row	Division Sentence
1	20	20 ÷ 1 = 20
2	10	20 ÷ 2 = 10

   B. Use your table to help you list the factors of 20.
   C. Look back at Lesson 1, Question 1 in the Homework section on page 100. What do you notice about the table in Lesson 1 and this table? What is the same and what is different?

10. A. Make a table like the one in Question 9 to show all of the rectangles that can be made with 36 tiles.
    B. Use your table to help you list the factors of 36.

11. Find the factors of:
    A. 12   B. 16   C. 18

A **prime number** is any number greater than one that has only two factors—itself and one. Thirteen is a prime number because its only factors are 13 and 1. Fourteen is not a prime number because it has four factors: 1, 2, 7, and 14.

12. Which of the following are prime numbers? Explain.
    A. 35   B. 27   C. 41

104 SG · Grade 4 · Unit 4 · Lesson 2   Factors

Student Guide - Page 104

Content Note

Testing Whether a Number Is Prime. When testing whether a number is prime, it is not necessary to look for factors any larger than the square root of the number. To see that this is true, consider the list below of numbers whose product is 36. As the list continues, the numbers on the left increase and the numbers on the right decrease, but in each pair, there is always one number less than 6, the square root of 36.

$$1 \times 36$$
$$2 \times 18$$
$$3 \times 12$$
$$4 \times 9$$
$$5 \times 7.2$$
$$6 \times 6$$
$$7 \times 5.14 \ldots$$
$$8 \times 4.5$$
$$9 \times 4$$
$$10 \times 3.6$$

When testing whether 41 is prime, for example, we only have to test numbers less than 7 (the square root of 41 is about 6.4), since if 41 had any factors, at least one of them would be less than 7.

This is also a good way to determine whether all of the factors of a particular number have been found. Consider the same list, but omit the cases that don't result in whole numbers.

$$1 \times 36$$
$$2 \times 18$$
$$3 \times 12$$
$$4 \times 9$$
$$6 \times 6$$

Once the square root is reached, all the factors are now listed in order by reading in a U starting at the upper left and finishing at the upper right. 1, 2, 3, 4, 6, 9, 12, 18, 36. Now consider the factors of 24, using the same system.

$$1 \times 24$$
$$2 \times 12$$
$$3 \times 8$$
$$4 \times 6$$

The next number to be tested is 5, but that does not have a whole number partner. The next number is 6, but that factor has already been identified in the 4×6 sentence. Therefore, all the factors of 24 have now been identified, reading in order from the upper left 1, 2, 3, 4, 6, 8, 12, 24. Once a number on the left is the same as one on the right, the task is completed and all the factors have been identified.

Students are then asked to consider which of 35, 27, and 41 are prime. They can solve this by searching for factors, either with calculators or by building arrays. They will find that 5 divides 35 evenly and 3 divides 27 evenly. They will be unable to find any factors of 41 other than 1 and 41, so it is prime.

Encourage students to be systematic when they search for prime numbers. For example, when they search for the factors of 41, they should test the numbers in order: $41 \div 2 = 20.5$ so 2 is not a factor (since 20.5 is not a whole number), $41 \div 3 = 13.67$ so 3 is not a factor, $41 \div 4 = 10.25$ so 4 is not a factor, and so on.

Some students will see pretty quickly that they don't need to test all the numbers up to 41 to be sure it is prime. Some students will see that they don't have to test any numbers greater than half of 41. Testing for factors up to half of a number is reasonable for students. Some students may realize they don't even need to test that far.

Suggestions for Teaching the Lesson

Math Facts

DPP Bit G provides practice with fact families for the twos and threes. The review on fact families dovetails nicely with the work on the rectangles chart in this lesson. DPP Task J provides math facts practice in solving a word problem.

Homework and Practice

- Assign the More Tile Problems section of the Homework section after Part 1 of this lesson. Students should have a sheet of *Square-Inch Grid Paper* to help them solve the problems.

- Assign the More Finding Factors Problems section after Part 2 of this lesson. Students should have calculators, grid paper, and multiplication tables available to help solve these problems.

- DPP Task H supports the content of this lesson by exploring the area of square figures measured in English units.

- DPP Bit I is a word problem involving time.

Homework

More Tile Problems

Use *Square-Inch Grid Paper* to help you solve these problems. Write a number sentence to go with each problem.

1. Irma made a rectangle with 28 tiles. If there were 7 rows, how many tiles were in each row?

2. Keenya made a rectangle with 8 rows and 5 tiles in each row. How many tiles did she use?

3. Romesh made a rectangle with 42 tiles. There were 6 tiles in each row. How many rows were there?

4. A rectangle of 18 tiles has 3 different colors. There is an equal number of each color. How many of each color are there?

More Finding Factors Problems

5. A. Make a table like the one at right to show the rectangles that can be made with 28 tiles. You can use a calculator, multiplication facts, or *Square-Inch Grid Paper* to help you divide.

Rectangles Possible with 28 Tiles

Number of Rows	Number in Each Row	Division Sentence
1	28	28 ÷ 1 = 28
2	14	28 ÷ 2 = 14

   B. Use the table to help you list the factors of 28.

6. A. Make a table similar to that in Question 5 to show the rectangles that can be made with 40 tiles.
   B. List the factors of 40.

7. A. Is 3 a factor of 27? How do you know?
   B. Is 7 a factor of 32? How do you know?

8. List all the factors of:
   A. 6
   B. 30
   C. 32

Factors   SG · Grade 4 · Unit 4 · Lesson 2 105

Student Guide - Page 105

Daily Practice and Problems: Tasks for Lesson 2

H. Task: Counting Square Units
(URG p. 15)

1. How many square inches are there in one square foot? The sketch below may help you.

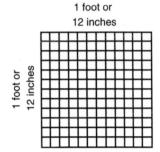

1 foot or 12 inches

1 foot or 12 inches

2. How many square feet are in one square yard? Draw a sketch to help you.
   (*Hint:* 3 feet = 1 yard)

J. Task: Going to the Movies
(URG p. 16)

1. Roberto went to the movies on Saturday with his mother, father, and his 2 younger sisters. Tickets cost $6.00 for adults and $4.50 for children. How much did it cost the family to go to the movies?

2. Prices on Tuesdays are only $4.50 for adults and $3.00 for children. How much will Roberto's family save if they go to the movies on Tuesday instead of Saturday?

9. Help the Sunny Fruit Company design a rectangular-shaped box for shipping four dozen oranges. (How many oranges are in four dozen?) How many layers will your box have, how many rows of oranges will be in each layer, and how many oranges will be in each row? (There is more than one way to do this.)

10. Which of the following are prime numbers? How do you know?
    A. 39
    B. 51
    C. 67

11. Challenge question: Find all the prime numbers between 25 and 50. Explain what you did to find your answer.

Student Guide - Page 106

Use the *Observational Assessment Record* to record students' abilities to use arrays to represent multiplication and division problems and to determine whether one number is a factor of another.

AT A GLANCE

Math Facts and Daily Practice and Problems

DPP items G and J provide practice with math facts for the twos and threes. Task H provides practice with square units. Bit I involves time.

Part 1. Tile Problems

Students solve *Questions 1–4* in the Tile Problems section of the *Factors* Activity Pages in the *Student Guide.*

Part 2. Finding Factors

1. Discuss what rectangles are possible with various numbers of rows. This leads to a discussion of factors, including a way to find factors using a calculator.
2. Students find factors of 24 by listing the dimensions of all rectangles that can be made from 24 tiles. (Class repeats for 28 tiles if necessary.)
3. Read together the definitions of factors in the Finding Factors section of the *Factors* Activity Pages.
4. Students answer *Questions 5–12* in the *Student Guide.* Questions involve factors and prime numbers.

Homework

1. Assign the More Tiles Problems section of the Homework section in the *Student Guide* after Part 1.
2. Assign the More Finding Factors Problems section of the Homework section after Part 2.

Assessment

Use the *Observational Assessment Record* to record students' abilities to use rectangular arrays to represent multiplication and division problems and to find the factors of a number, using either an array or a calculator.

Notes:

Student Guide

Questions 1–12 (SG pp. 102–104)

1. 8 tiles; $4 \times 8 = 32$

2. 30 tiles; $6 \times 5 = 30$

3. 3 rows; $3 \times 7 = 21$

4. 4 tiles of each color; $4 \times 3 = 12$

5. **A.** Yes; 4 tiles in each row; $24 \div 6 = 4$

   B. No; $24 \div 7 = 3.4285714\ldots$; The answer on the calculator is not a whole number.

6. **A.** No; Explanations will vary. Using the calculator: $38 \div 5 = 7.6$; You cannot make a rectangle with 5 rows and 38 tiles.

   B. Yes; Explanations will vary. Using the calculator: $35 \div 5 = 7$—a whole number. You can make a rectangle with 5 rows and 35 tiles. There would be 7 tiles in each row.

7. **A.** Yes; Explanations will vary. $32 \div 8 = 4$; You can make a rectangle with 8 rows and 32 tiles. There would be 4 tiles in each row.

   B. No; Explanations will vary. $36 \div 8 = 4.5$; You cannot make a rectangle with 8 rows and 36 tiles.

8. **A.** Yes; Yes; $48 \div 6 = 8$; 8 students in each row

   B. No; No; $48 \div 7 = 6.8571429\ldots$

   C. Yes; Yes; $48 \div 8 = 6$; 6 students in each row

9. **A.** Rectangles Possible with 20 Tiles

Number of Rows	Number in Each Row	Division Sentence
1	20	$20 \div 1 = 20$
2	10	$20 \div 2 = 10$
4	5	$20 \div 4 = 5$
5	4	$20 \div 5 = 4$
10	2	$20 \div 10 = 2$
20	1	$20 \div 20 = 1$

B. 1, 2, 4, 5, 10, 20

C. The first two columns are the same. The third column has multiplication sentences in Lesson 1 and division problems in Lesson 2.

10. **A.** Rectangles Possible with 36 Tiles

Number of Rows	Number in Each Row	Division Sentence
1	36	$36 \div 1 = 36$
2	18	$36 \div 2 = 18$
3	12	$36 \div 3 = 12$
4	9	$36 \div 4 = 9$
6	6	$36 \div 6 = 6$
9	4	$36 \div 9 = 4$
12	3	$36 \div 12 = 3$
18	2	$36 \div 18 = 2$
36	1	$36 \div 36 = 1$

B. 1, 2, 3, 4, 6, 9, 12, 18, 36

11. **A.** 1, 2, 3, 4, 6, 12

   B. 1, 2, 4, 8, 16

   C. 1, 2, 3, 6, 9, 18

12. **A.** *No; Explanations will vary. 35 has more than 2 factors (1, 5, 7, 35)

   B. *No; Explanations will vary. 27 has more than 2 factors (1, 3, 9, 27)

   C. *Yes; Explanations will vary. Systematic testing for factors shows that 41 has only 2 factors (1 and 41).

---

*Answers and/or discussion are included in the Lesson Guide.

**Answers for all the Home Practice in the *Discovery Assignment Book* are at the end of the unit.

Homework (SG pp. 105–106)

Questions 1–11

1. 4 tiles; $28 \div 7 = 4$
2. 40 tiles; $8 \times 5 = 40$
3. 7 rows; $42 \div 6 = 7$
4. 6 tiles of each color; $18 \div 3 = 6$
5. **A.** Rectangles Possible with 28 Tiles

Number of Rows	Number in Each Row	Division Sentence
1	28	$28 \div 1 = 28$
2	14	$28 \div 2 = 14$
4	7	$28 \div 4 = 7$
7	4	$28 \div 7 = 4$
14	2	$28 \div 14 = 2$
28	1	$28 \div 28 = 1$

   B. 1, 2, 4, 7, 14, 28

6. **A.** Rectangles Possible with 40 Tiles

Number of Rows	Number in Each Row	Division Sentence
1	40	$40 \div 1 = 40$
2	20	$40 \div 2 = 20$
4	10	$40 \div 4 = 10$
5	8	$40 \div 5 = 8$
8	5	$40 \div 8 = 5$
10	4	$40 \div 10 = 4$
20	2	$40 \div 20 = 2$
40	1	$40 \div 40 = 1$

   B. 1, 2, 4, 5, 8, 10, 20, 40

7. **A.** Yes; Explanations will vary. $3 \times 9 = 27$; If you skip count by 3s you hit 27. You can make a rectangle with 3 rows and 27 tiles. 9 tiles would be in each row.

   B. No; Explanations will vary. $32 \div 7 = 4.5714 \ldots$; You cannot make a rectangle with 7 rows and 32 tiles.

8. **A.** 1, 2, 3, 6

   B. 1, 2, 3, 5, 6, 10, 15, 30

   C. 1, 2, 4, 8, 16, 32

9. 48 oranges need to be boxed; Designs of boxes vary. Two of the possible solutions are:

   4 layers of oranges, each layer has 12 oranges arranged in 3 rows of 4 oranges;

   3 layers of oranges, each layer has 16 oranges arranged in 4 rows of 4 oranges

10. **A.** No; Explanations will vary. 39 has four factors: 1, 3, 13, and 39. You can make more than one rectangle with 39 tiles.

    B. No; Explanations will vary. 51 has four factors: 1, 3, 17, and 51. You can make more than one rectangle with 51 tiles.

    C. Yes; Explanations will vary. A systematic check for factors shows that 67 only has 1 and itself as factors. (See Content Note in Lesson Guide 2 for a discussion of testing whether a number is prime.)

11. 29, 31, 37, 41, 43, and 47. Solution strategies will vary.

*Answers and/or discussion are included in the Lesson Guide.

**Answers for all the Home Practice in the *Discovery Assignment Book* are at the end of the unit.

LESSON GUIDE

Floor Tiler

Estimated Class Sessions: 1

Each player spins two numbers and uses the product of the numbers to color in rectangles on grid paper. Players take turns spinning and filling in rectangles until someone fills in the grid completely.

Key Content

- Practicing multiplication facts.
- Representing multiplication problems using arrays.

Key Vocabulary

product

Materials List

Print Materials for Students

	Math Facts and Daily Practice and Problems	Game	Written Assessment
Student Books — Student Guide		*Floor Tiler* Pages 107–108	
Student Books — Discovery Assignment Book		*Spinners 1–4 and 1–10* Page 47	
Teacher Resources — Facts Resource Guide ⊙	DPP Items 4K–4L		
Teacher Resources — Unit Resource Guide	DPP Items K–L Pages 16–17 ⊙		DPP Bit K *Multiples of a Number* Page 16 ⊙
Teacher Resources — Generic Section ⊙		*Small Multiplication Tables,* 2 per student (1 for class, 1 for home) and *Centimeter Grid Paper,* 2–3 per student pair	

⊙ *available on Teacher Resource CD*

All Transparency Masters, Blackline Masters, and Assessment Blackline Masters in the Unit Resource Guide are on the Teacher Resource CD.

Supplies for Each Student Pair

clear plastic spinner (or pencil with paper clip)

Supplies for Each Student

crayon or marker
calculator
scissors

Materials for the Teacher

Transparency of *Centimeter Grid Paper* (Unit Resource Guide, Generic Section), optional
Transparency of *Spinners 1–4 and 1–10* Game Page (Discovery Assignment Book) Page 47, optional extension

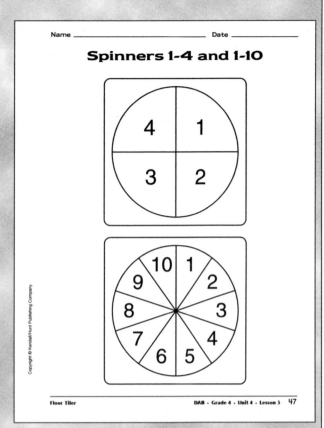

4   1

3   2

10 1 2 3 4 5 6 7 8 9

Discovery Assignment Book - Page 47

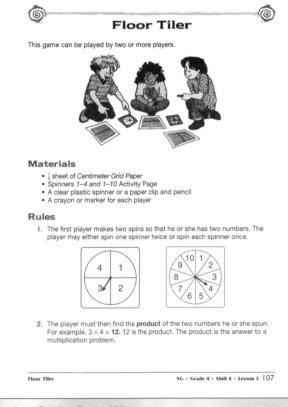

◎ ═══════════════════ ◎

Floor Tiler

This game can be played by two or more players.

Materials

- ½ sheet of *Centimeter Grid Paper*
- *Spinners 1–4 and 1–10* Activity Page
- A clear plastic spinner or a paper clip and pencil
- A crayon or marker for each player

Rules

1. The first player makes two spins so that he or she has two numbers. The player may either spin one spinner twice or spin each spinner once.

4 1
3 2

10 1 2 3 4 5 6 7 8 9

2. The player must then find the **product** of the two numbers he or she spun. For example, 3 × 4 = **12.** 12 is the product. The product is the answer to a multiplication problem.

Student Guide - Page 107

Before the Activity

Each student will need a half-sheet of *Centimeter Grid Paper.* Hand out copies of the sheet, instructing student pairs to cut the grid in half. Or, cut the sheets ahead of time. Partners should check that their half-sheets have the same number of rows.

If you do not have clear plastic spinners to place over the *Spinners 1–4 and 1–10* Game Page, students can use paper clips and pencils. Straighten out one end of the paper clip, and place a pencil through the curved end of the paper clip. Then, put the point of the pencil on the center of the spinner, and spin the paper clip around the pencil, using the straightened end as the pointer. See Figure 8.

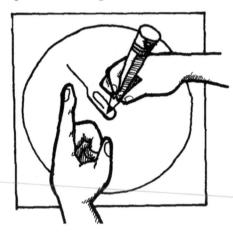

Figure 8: *Using a paper clip and pencil as a spinner*

In class, each student should have one multiplication table from the *Small Multiplication Tables* Activity Page available as a reference for this game. Students should also take home one of the small multiplication tables so they can play this game at home. The students may also use their copies of the *Multiplication Facts I Know* chart, which were distributed in Unit 3, or calculators.

Developing the Activity

The rules for playing the game are found on the *Floor Tiler* Game Pages in the *Student Guide.* A student spins to find two numbers for a multiplication sentence. He or she may use either two spins from one spinner or one spin from each spinner. After finding the product, the player colors in a rectangle with that number of squares, outlines this rectangle and records its number sentence inside. The rectangles must have the same number of squares as the product of the two numbers. However, the dimensions of the rectangles do not have to be the same as the two numbers spun. For example, if a player spins 6 and 3, he or she can draw either a 6×3, 18×1, or 9×2 rectangle—whichever fits best. Players continue in this fashion until one player fills in his or her grid completely. If a student is unable to fill in a rectangle given his or her product, the student loses that turn. You may want to demonstrate the game using a transparency of *Centimeter Grid Paper* while a volunteer spins the spinners.

A good strategy is to use two spins from Spinner 1–10 at the beginning of the game and two spins from Spinner 1–4 near the end of the game. This way, the player gets to fill in large rectangles when his or her grid is empty and small rectangles when space gets tight.

The students may find that it becomes difficult to fill in the grid completely when only a few squares are left. Encourage them to create a new rule to address this situation. For instance, if no player is able to color in a rectangle in three rounds of spinning, the player with the fewest squares left is the winner. This type of rule may be helpful if students find it hard to end the game.

Suggestions for Teaching the Lesson

Math Facts

DPP Bit K provides practice with math facts by finding multiples and factors. Task L provides practice with math facts in a word problem involving area.

Homework and Practice

Students can take home *Floor Tiles* Game Pages in the *Student Guide,* the *Spinners 1–4 and 1–10* Game Page, *Centimeter Grid Paper,* and a multiplication table to play the game at home. They may use pencil-and-paper-clip spinners. They can record the number of minutes they play with family members or friends.

3. After finding the product, the player colors in a rectangle that has the same number of grid squares on the grid paper. For example, he or she might color in 3 rows of 4 squares for a total of 12 squares. But the player could also color in 2 rows of 6 squares or 1 row of 12 squares. (Remember, the squares colored in must connect so that they form a rectangle.)

4. Once the player has made his or her rectangle, the player draws an outline around it and writes its number sentence inside. For example, a player who colored in 3 rows of 4 squares would write "$3 \times 4 = 12$." A player who colored in 2 rows of 6 squares would write "$2 \times 6 = 12$."

5. Players take turns spinning and filling in their grids.

6. If a player is unable to fill in a rectangle for his or her spin, that player loses the turn, and the next player can play.

7. The first player to fill in his or her grid paper completely wins the game.

108 SG · Grade 4 · Unit 4 · Lesson 3   Floor Tiler

Student Guide - Page 108

Daily Practice and Problems: Task for Lesson 3

L. Task: Tiling the Shower
(URG p. 17)

Myrna Myrmidon and her Aunt Penny want to tile 3 walls of their shower. Each wall is 3 inches by 2 inches. How many square-inch tiles will they need in all? If the tiles come in packages of 10, how many packages should they buy?

Assessment

Use DPP Bit K *Multiples of a Number* as a short assessment on factors and multiples.

Extension

You can also play this game as a class by using transparencies of *Spinners 1–4 and 1–10*. Each student will fill in a rectangle on his or her half-sheet of *Centimeter Grid Paper.* Since players will fill in the grid differently, they will finish at different times. The first to finish is the winner.

AT A GLANCE

Math Facts and Daily Practice and Problems

DPP items K and L both provide practice with math facts.

Developing the Activity

1. Read the directions on the *Floor Tiler* Game Pages in the *Student Guide.*
2. Demonstrate the game using a transparency of *Centimeter Grid Paper* while a volunteer spins the spinners on the *Spinners 1–4 and 1–10* Game Page from the *Discovery Assignment Book.*
3. Students play the game. As a reference, each student may use one of the tables from a copy of the *Small Multiplication Tables* Activity Page.

Homework

Students take home the *Floor Tiles* Game Pages in the *Student Guide,* the *Spinners 1–4 and 1–10* Game Page, *Centimeter Grid Paper,* and a small multiplication table. They play the game at home using pencil-and-paper-clip spinners.

Assessment

Use DPP Bit K as an assessment.

Notes:

LESSON GUIDE

Prime Factors

Estimated Class Sessions: 3–4

In their work up to this point, students have found products of two factors at a time. They begin this activity by finding products of three factors. Then, they consider the opposite question: given a number (with several factors), write it as a product of at least three factors. Factor trees are introduced to help students organize their work. This organization helps them to search in a systematic way for the prime factors of the number. To tie together the work they have done in the unit, students write and solve number puzzles that involve the words multiple, factor, and prime and square numbers. Finally, exponents are introduced as a shortcut for writing numbers as products.

Key Content

- Finding products of more than two factors.
- Using factor trees to find the prime factors of a number.
- Solving problems involving multiples, factors, prime and square numbers.
- Using exponents.
- Explaining mathematical reasoning.

Key Vocabulary

exponent
factor tree
prime factor
prime factorization

Curriculum Sequence

After This Unit

Exponents. Students use exponents in Unit 6 in their study of large numbers.

Daily Practice and Problems: Bits for Lesson 4

M. Making Rectangles with Tiles
(URG p. 17)

Make a table like the one below to show all the different rectangles that can be made with 54 tiles. You can use a calculator or multiplication facts to help you divide.

Number of Rows	Number in Each Row	Division Sentence
1	54	$54 \div 1 = 54$
2		$54 \div 2 =$

O. Play *Digits Game* (URG p. 18)

Play *Digits Game* for addition. Draw boxes like these on your paper. As your teacher or classmate chooses the digits, write them in the boxes. Try to find the largest sum. Remember that each digit will be read only once.

Q. Time Goes By (URG p. 19)

1. Nicholas arrived at   His dad picked
   his friend's house at: him up at:

   How long was Nicholas's visit?

2. Nicholas ate   He went to
   dinner at: bed at:

   How much time passed from dinner to bedtime?

DPP Tasks are on page 56. Suggestions for using the DPPs are on pages 55–56.

Materials List

Print Materials for Students

	Math Facts and Daily Practice and Problems	Activity	Homework	Written Assessment
Student Books				
Student Guide		*Prime Factors* Pages 109–114	*Prime Factors* Homework Section Pages 114–115	Student Rubric: *Telling* Appendix C and Inside Back Cover ⊙
Discovery Assignment Book			Home Practice Part 2 Page 39	
Teacher Resources				
Facts Resource Guide ⊙	DPP Items 4M & 4R			
Unit Resource Guide	DPP Items M–R Pages 17–20 ⊙			*Unit 4 Test* Pages 57–58, 1 per student
Generic Section ⊙		*Small Multiplication Tables,* 1 per student (to tape on desk)		

⊙ available on Teacher Resource CD

All Transparency Masters, Blackline Masters, and Assessment Blackline Masters in the Unit Resource Guide are on the Teacher Resource CD.

Supplies for Each Student

calculator
square-inch tiles

Developing the Activity

Part 1. Multiplying Three Factors

Begin the lesson by discussing the example illustrated in the picture on the *Prime Factors* Activity Pages in the *Student Guide.* There are $3 \times 4 \times 5$ apples in a crate with 5 layers and 3 rows of 4 in each layer. In *Question 1,* students discover that when multiplying more than two factors the way they group and order the factors will not change the answer. Point out that smart choices can make calculations easier. For example, when finding the product $4 \times 2 \times 5$, it might be easier to find $2 \times 5 = 10$ first and then multiply 4×10 to get the final answer. You can show this in writing as follows:

$$4 \times (2 \times 5) = 40$$
$$4 \times 10 = 40$$

In *Question 2,* students find products of 3 factors, in any way they choose. Allow them to use mental math, calculators, or multiplication tables. *Question 1* in the Homework section provides additional practice in finding products of three factors.

Part 2. Finding Prime Factors

Ask your students to think of different ways to write 24 as a product of two or more factors, as Mrs. Dewey did in the Finding Prime Factors section of the *Prime Factors* Activity Pages in the *Student Guide.* If some students find factors that are all prime numbers, ask them to tell how they found their answers. If none of your students find all **prime factors,** choose one of their answers and ask whether any of the factors can be factored into smaller numbers. For example, in the sentence $24 = 3 \times 4 \times 2$, the 4 can be factored into 2×2. The sentence then becomes $24 = 3 \times 2 \times 2 \times 2$. This is how Nicholas listed prime factors on the *Prime Factors* Activity Pages.

Show the class how to use a **factor tree** to organize the work in a search for factors. You can draw the tree that Mrs. Dewey drew to match Nicholas's work or the example in Figure 9. This is the tree that John uses in *Question 3.*

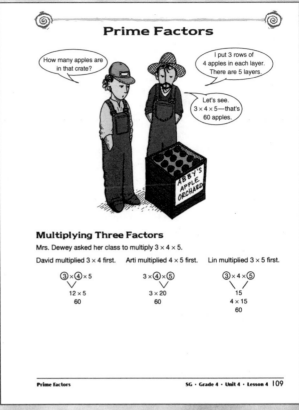

Student Guide - Page 109

Student Guide - Page 110

Student Guide - Page 111

Mrs. Dewey showed another way to write Nicholas's solution. She used a **factor tree**.

She factored 24 into 3 × 8. She circled the 3 because it cannot be factored anymore (it is prime). She factored 8 into 4 × 2 and circled the 2 because it is prime. She factored 4 into 2 × 2 and circled the 2s. She multiplied the circled numbers and got the same answer as Nicholas: 24 = 3 × 2 × 2 × 2.

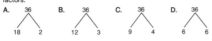

Nila decided to use a factor tree to show her solution. She factored 24 into 6 × 4. She decided not to write the multiplication signs in her factor tree. That was O.K.

She factored 6 into 2 × 3 and 4 into 2 × 2. She circled the 2s and the 3 because they were prime and could not be factored anymore.

She multiplied the prime numbers she had circled and got: 24 = 2 × 3 × 2 × 2.

Nila's answer was the same as Nicholas's, even though her factor tree was different.

3. John started the following factor tree for 24. Continue building his tree until all the numbers are prime. What factorization does your tree give you of 24?

Student Guide - Page 111

Student Guide - Page 112

4. Complete the following factor trees for 36. Write 36 as a product of its prime factors.

  A. 36 / 18 2   B. 36 / 12 3   C. 36 / 9 4   D. 36 / 6 6

5. Use factor trees to factor each of the following numbers into primes. Write number sentences to show your answers.
  A. 18
  B. 12
  C. 56
  D. 90

6. I am a prime number between 10 and 20. I am one more than a square number. What number am I?

7. I am a multiple of 3. I am a square number. I am less than 20. What number am I?

8. I am a multiple of 5. Two is not one of my factors. I am not prime and I am not square. I am less than 30. What number am I?

Did You Know?

Some mathematicians study ways to factor large numbers. This is part of a branch of mathematics called number theory. Mathematicians study number theory because it is fun and interesting. Many of the discoveries that mathematicians made about number theory later turned out to be very useful. For example, factoring is important in making and breaking secret codes.

Student Guide - Page 112

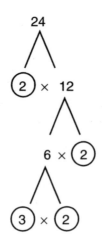

Factor 24 into 2 × 12. Circle the 2 to show it cannot be factored anymore (it is prime).

Factor 12 into 6 × 2 and circle the 2 because it is prime.

Factor 6 into 3 × 2 and circle the 2 and the 3.

Multiply the circled numbers to get 24 = 2 × 2 × 3 × 2.

Figure 9: *A factor tree for 24*

The *Prime Factors* Activity Pages give examples of factor trees for 24, starting with 3 × 8, 6 × 4, and 2 × 12. For additional class practice, work together to make factor trees for 30 and 40. When students are ready, ask them to answer *Questions 4–5,* which provide additional practice with factor trees. Students can discuss their solutions with partners.

Questions 6–8 are number puzzles that give clues using the words multiple, factor, prime number, and square number. These number puzzles are good problems for the students to work on together. Have them explain their solution paths, telling why they rejected any alternative solutions. Review the Student Rubric: *Telling* to help students organize their thinking.

Assign *Questions 1–7* of the Homework section at this time. *Questions 2–3* in the Homework section of the *Prime Factors* Activity Pages provide additional practice with factoring. *Questions 4–6* are additional number puzzles and *Question 7* asks students to write their own number puzzles. Plan to spend a few minutes for the next few days having students solve each other's puzzles.

If your students need additional factor tree practice, ask them to make factor trees for the numbers 42, 56, 66, 90, 196, and 1000.

Part 3. Exponents

When students factor numbers with repeated factors, such as $32 = 2 \times 2 \times 2 \times 2 \times 2$, introduce **exponents** as a shortcut for writing the factors. The Exponents section of the *Prime Factors* Activity Pages provides students with examples. It is not important that all students use the exponential notation at this time, but some will choose to use it. In *Questions 9–12,* they practice this notation and find the prime factors of a few more numbers. Assign *Questions 8–10* in the Homework section after this part for additional practice.

Part 4. Tying It Together

Spend the remainder of the time in this lesson practicing factoring and solving the number puzzles students wrote for *Question 7* in the Homework section. Review the Student Rubric: *Telling* again before students take the *Unit 4 Test*. The last question asks students to use this rubric.

Suggestions for Teaching the Lesson

Math Facts

DPP Bit M provides another opportunity for students to find the factors of a number using a three-column table and rectangular arrays. Task R is a collection of math riddles that practice math facts and develop number sense.

---

9. Rewrite the following factorizations using exponents:
   A. $600 = 2 \times 2 \times 2 \times 3 \times 5 \times 5$
   B. $378 = 2 \times 3 \times 3 \times 3 \times 7$
   C. $250 = 2 \times 5 \times 5 \times 5$
   D. $99 = 3 \times 3 \times 11$

10. Use exponents to rewrite each factorization you found in Question 5.

11. Write each of the following products without using exponents. Then multiply.
    A. $2^3 \times 3$
    B. $3^2 \times 5$
    C. 2×5^2
    D. $7^2 \times 2$

12. Find the prime factors of each of the following numbers. Write your answers using exponents.
    A. 100
    B. 40
    C. 80
    D. 500

Homework

Dear Family Member:

This Homework section contains work with factors and multiplication. Background information about factors, prime numbers, and factor trees can be found in the previous pages of this section.

1. Find the products. You may use mental math, a calculator, or your multiplication table.
   A. $2 \times 3 \times 3 =$ B. $3 \times 2 \times 3 =$
   C. $2 \times 2 \times 2 =$ D. $3 \times 3 \times 5 =$
   E. $3 \times 3 \times 3 =$ F. $2 \times 2 \times 5 =$
   G. $3 \times 2 \times 5 =$ H. $7 \times 3 \times 2 =$
   I. $5 \times 4 \times 3 =$ J. $3 \times 4 \times 2 =$

Student Guide - Page 114

Exponents

Lee Yah factored 45 into prime factors. She wrote $45 = 5 \times 3 \times 3$. Linda found the same prime factors of 45 but wrote them using an exponent: $45 = 5 \times 3^2$.

John factored 32. He wrote $32 = 2 \times 2 \times 2 \times 2 \times 2$. He wondered whether there was a shortcut for writing this. Mrs. Dewey showed how exponents can be used as a shortcut for writing products of the same factor:

$2 \times 2 \times 2 = 2^3$ (We read this as "2 cubed" or "two to the third power.")

Three is the **exponent**. Two is the **base**. The exponent tells us to multiply by 2, three times.

$2 \times 2 \times 2 \times 2 = 2^4$ (We read this as "two to the fourth power.")

$2 \times 2 \times 2 \times 2 \times 2 = 2^5$ (We read this as "two to the fifth power.")

How would you use this shortcut to write $3 \times 3 \times 3 \times 3$?

Jerome factored 72. He wrote $72 = 3 \times 3 \times 2 \times 2 \times 2$. Then, he wrote this with exponents: $72 = 3^2 \times 2^3$.

Student Guide - Page 113

---

2. Determine which of the following are prime numbers. If a number is prime, tell how you know. If it is not prime, write it as the product of prime factors.
   A. 6   B. 17
   C. 12   D. 39

3. Use factor trees to factor each of the following numbers into primes. Write multiplication sentences to show your answers.
   A. 20   B. 28   C. 60   D. 48
   E. 54   F. 72   G. 100   H. 42

4. I am a multiple of 2. I am not a multiple of 3. I am greater than 10 but less than 20. I am not a square number. What number am I?

5. I am between 6 and 35. I am one more than a square number. Five is one of my factors. What number am I?

6. I am the smallest square number that has the factors 2 and 3. What number am I?

7. Write your own number puzzle, similar to the ones in Questions 4–6. Use some of the following words: multiple, factor, prime number, square number.

8. Rewrite the following factorizations using exponents:
   A. $200 = 2 \times 5 \times 5 \times 2 \times 2$
   B. $600 = 2 \times 3 \times 2 \times 5 \times 2 \times 5$
   C. $1200 = 2 \times 2 \times 3 \times 2 \times 2 \times 5 \times 5$
   D. $1500 = 2 \times 5 \times 2 \times 5 \times 5 \times 3$

9. Write each of the following products without exponents. Then multiply.
   A. $2^2 \times 3^2$ B. $3^3 \times 4^2$
   C. $2^3 \times 5^2$ D. $2^4 \times 3$

10. Find the prime factorizations of each of the following numbers. Write your answers using exponents.
    A. 50   B. 66
    C. 96   D. 300

Student Guide - Page 115

Daily Practice and Problems:
Tasks for Lesson 4

N. Task: Making Brownies
(URG p. 18)

Jenny plans to make 2 batches of
brownies for her class's bake sale.
There are 32 brownies in a batch.

If she puts 4 brownies in each bag and
each bag sells for 50¢, how much money
will her class make selling Jenny's brownies?

P. Task: Addition and Subtraction
(URG p. 19)

Use a paper-and-pencil method or mental
math to find exact answers to these problems.
Estimate to see if your answers make sense.

1. A. $\begin{array}{r} 4356 \\ -\ 436 \\ \hline \end{array}$ B. $\begin{array}{r} 5236 \\ +\ \ 89 \\ \hline \end{array}$

   C. $\begin{array}{r} 4296 \\ +2907 \\ \hline \end{array}$ D. $\begin{array}{r} 34,500 \\ -\ 4003 \\ \hline \end{array}$

2. Explain your strategy for a problem you
   solved using mental math.

R. Task: What Numbers Are We?
(URG p. 20)

1. I am more than 50 and less than 60.
   Both my digits are the same. Who am I?

2. I am more than 2×45 and less than
   2×50. If you skip count by 5s you will
   hit me. Who am I?

3. I am even. I am less than 3×6 but more
   than 3×5. Who am I?

4. Make up your own riddle. Write it down
   and trade with a friend. Can you solve
   your friend's riddle?

Homework and Practice

- Assign the problems in the Homework section of
  the *Prime Factors* Activity Pages in the *Student
  Guide*. Assign **Questions 1–7** after Parts 1 and 2
  and **Questions 8–10** after Part 3. They are very
  similar to the problems intended for class work.
  In **Question 7,** students write their own number
  puzzles. Allow time for students to solve each
  other's puzzles. Review the Student Rubric:
  Telling for students to use in explaining their
  solution paths.

- DPP Task N presents a multistep word problem
  requiring computational skills. Bit O is a replay of
  the *Digits Game* for addition. Task P is an exercise
  in multidigit addition and subtraction, using either
  paper and pencil or mental math. Bit Q provides
  practice calculating the passage of time.

- Assign Part 2 of the Home Practice.

*Answers for Part 2 of the Home Practice can be found in
the Answer Key at the end of this lesson and at the end of
this unit.*

Assessment

Use the *Unit 4 Test* Assessment Pages to assess your
students' knowledge of the material in this unit. The
last question asks students to use the TIMS Student
Rubric: *Telling* to help organize their thinking. Review
the rubric with them before they begin the test.

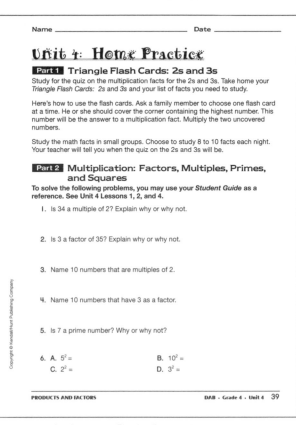

Discovery Assignment Book - Page 39

AT A GLANCE

Math Facts and Daily Practice and Problems

DPP Bit M provides further practice in finding factors. DPP items N, O, and P all provide computation practice. DPP Bit Q involves elapsed time. DPP Task R provides practice with math facts.

Part 1. Multiplying Three Factors

1. Students observe that the way they group and order factors when they multiply does not affect the product. *(Question 1)*
2. Students find products of three one-digit factors *(Question 2)*. They can use mental math, calculators, or multiplication tables as needed.

Part 2. Finding Prime Factors

1. Students write 24 as a product of two or more factors. Discuss different answers.
2. Students factor products further, until prime factors are found.
3. Introduce factor trees to organize work.
4. Discuss examples of factor trees from the Finding Prime Factors section in the *Student Guide*. Complete *Question 3* together. For additional practice, students use factor trees to find prime factors of 30 and 40.
5. Students answer *Questions 4–5* for practice with factor trees.
6. Students solve the number puzzles in *Questions 6–8* and review the Student Rubric: *Telling*.
7. For more factor tree practice, students factor 42, 56, 66, 90, 196, and 1000.

Part 3. Exponents

1. Introduce exponents as a shortcut for writing products with repeated factors.
2. Students practice by solving *Questions 9–12* in the Exponents section.

Part 4. Tying It Together

Students practice factoring and solve number puzzles written for homework in *Question 7*.

Homework

1. Assign *Questions 1–7* in the Homework section after Parts 1 and 2.
2. Assign homework *Questions 8–10* after Part 3.
3. Assign Part 2 of the Home Practice.

Assessment

Use the *Unit 4 Test* Assessment Pages in the *Unit Resource Guide* as an assessment.

Notes:

Unit 4 Test

You may use calculators, multiplication tables, or square-inch tiles to solve the following problems.

1. Danny made a rectangle with 40 tiles. If there were 5 rows, how many tiles were in each row? Draw a picture of this rectangle.

2. **A.** Is it possible to make a rectangle with 30 tiles and 6 rows? Why or why not?

   B. Is it possible to make a rectangle with 30 tiles and 4 rows? Why or why not?

3. List all the factors of 28. Show how you found your answer.

4. Which of the following are prime numbers? Tell how you know.

   A. 17

   B. 39

   C. 51

5. Design a box for the TIMS Candy Company that will hold 48 pieces of candy and that has more than two layers. Tell how many layers are in your box. Also, tell how many pieces of candy are in each layer. Each layer must hold the same number of pieces.

6. Use a factor tree to find the prime factors of 60.

7. Solve the following number puzzle. Write a paragraph about how you found your answer. Use the Student Rubric: *Telling* to help organize your thinking.

   I am a multiple of 3.
   2 is not one of my factors.
   I am not prime and I am not square.
   I am less than 20.
   What number am I?

Student Guide

Questions 1–12 (SG pp. 110–114)

1. A. *Multiply 2 × 2 first:
2 × 2 × 3 = 4 × 3 = 12. Multiply 2 × 3
first: 2 × 2 × 3 = 2 × 6 = 12.

B. 2 × 3 × 3 = 6 × 3 = 18 or
2 × 3 × 3 = 2 × 9 = 18

2. A. 20
B. 30
C. 27
D. 50
E. 40
F. 24
G. 90
H. 36

*3. 2 × 2 × 2 × 3, in any order. Two possible
factor trees are:

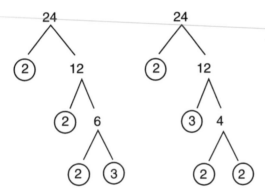

4. A. Factor trees will vary. One possible factor
tree follows. 2 × 2 × 3 × 3 in any order.

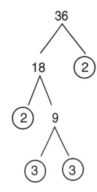

B. Factor trees will vary. One possible factor
tree follows. 2 × 2 × 3 × 3 in any order.

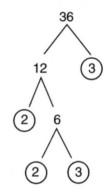

C. 2 × 2 × 3 × 3 in any order.

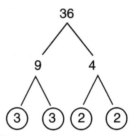

D. 2 × 2 × 3 × 3 in any order.

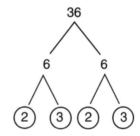

5. Check students' factor trees for each of
the following.
A. 2 × 3 × 3 = 18, in any order.
B. 2 × 2 × 3 = 12, in any order.
C. 2 × 2 × 2 × 7 = 56, in any order.
D. 2 × 3 × 3 × 5 = 90, in any order.

6. 17
7. 9
8. 15
9. A. $600 = 2^3 \times 3 \times 5^2$
B. $378 = 2 \times 3^3 \times 7$
C. $250 = 2 \times 5^3$
D. $99 = 3^2 \times 11$

---

*Answers and/or discussion are included in the Lesson Guide.
**Answers for all the Home Practice in the *Discovery Assignment Book* are at the end of the unit.

10. $18 = 2 \times 3^2$, $12 = 2^2 \times 3$, $56 = 2^3 \times 7$,
$90 = 2 \times 3^2 \times 5$

11. **A.** $2 \times 2 \times 2 \times 3 = 24$
  B. $3 \times 3 \times 5 = 45$
  C. $2 \times 5 \times 5 = 50$
  D. $7 \times 7 \times 2 = 98$

12. **A.** $2^2 \times 5^2$
  B. $2^3 \times 5$
  C. $2^4 \times 5$
  D. $2^2 \times 5^3$

Homework (SG pp. 114–115)

Questions 1–10

1. **A.** 18
  B. 18
  C. 8
  D. 45
  E. 27
  F. 20
  G. 30
  H. 42
  I. 60
  J. 24

2. **A.** 6 is not prime. $2 \times 3 = 6$
  B. 17 is prime. Its only factors are 1 and itself.
  C. 12 is not prime. $2 \times 2 \times 3 = 12$
  D. 39 is not prime. $3 \times 13 = 39$

3. Check students' factor trees for each of the following.
  A. $2 \times 2 \times 5 = 20$, in any order.
  B. $2 \times 2 \times 7 = 28$, in any order.
  C. $2 \times 2 \times 3 \times 5 = 60$, in any order.
  D. $2 \times 2 \times 2 \times 2 \times 3 = 48$, in any order.
  E. $2 \times 3 \times 3 \times 3 = 54$, in any order.
  F. $2 \times 2 \times 2 \times 3 \times 3 = 72$, in any order.
  G. $2 \times 2 \times 5 \times 5 = 100$, in any order.
  H. $2 \times 3 \times 7 = 42$, in any order.

4. 14

5. 10

6. 36

7. Answers will vary.

8. **A.** $200 = 2^3 \times 5^2$
  B. $600 = 2^3 \times 3 \times 5^2$
  C. $1200 = 2^4 \times 3 \times 5^2$
  D. $1500 = 2^2 \times 3 \times 5^3$

9. **A.** $2 \times 2 \times 3 \times 3 = 36$
  B. $3 \times 3 \times 3 \times 4 \times 4 = 432$
  C. $2 \times 2 \times 5 \times 5 = 100$
  D. $2 \times 2 \times 2 \times 2 \times 3 = 48$

10. **A.** $2 \times 5^2 = 50$, in any order.
  B. $2 \times 3 \times 11 = 66$
  C. $2^5 \times 3 = 96$
  D. $2^2 \times 3 \times 5^2 = 300$

Discovery Assignment Book

**Home Practice (DAB p. 39)

Part 2. Multiplication: Factors, Multiples, Primes, and Squares

Questions 1–6

1. Yes. Explanations will vary. One possible explanation is that 34 is an even number and all even numbers are multiples of 2.

2. No. Explanations will vary. Possible explanations: 1, 5, 7, and 35 are the factors of 35. 3 does not divide evenly into 35.

3. Answers will vary. All even numbers: 2, 4, 6, 8, 10, 12, 14, 16, 18 . . .

4. Answers will vary. All multiples of 3: 3, 6, 9, 12, 15, 18, 21, 24 . . .

5. Yes. Explanations will vary. One possible explanation is that 7 has no other factors but 1 and itself.

6. **A.** 25
  B. 100
  C. 4
  D. 9

---

*Answers and/or discussion are included in the Lesson Guide.

**Answers for all the Home Practice in the *Discovery Assignment Book* are at the end of the unit.

Unit Resource Guide

Unit 4 Test (URG pp. 58–59)

Questions 1–7

1. 8 tiles

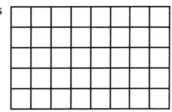

2. **A.** Yes. Explanations will vary. $30 \div 6 = 5$.

   B. No. Explanations will vary. $30 \div 4 = 7$ remainder 2. 4 does not evenly divide 30.

3. 1, 2, 4, 7, 14, 28. Solution strategies will vary. $28 \div 1 = 28$, $28 \div 2 = 14$, $28 \div 4 = 7$, $28 \div 7 = 4$, $28 \div 14 = 2$, $28 \div 1 = 28$.

4. **A.** 17 is a prime number. Its only factors are 1 and itself.

   B. 39 is not a prime number. It has 1, 3, 13, and 39 as factors.

   C. 51 is not a prime number. It has 1, 3, 17, and 51 as factors.

5. Boxes will vary. Some possible boxes include: 3 layers with 16 candies each, 4 layers with 12 candies each, 6 layers with 8 candies each, etc.

6. Factor trees will vary. 60 as a product of primes: $2 \times 2 \times 3 \times 5$. Some possible trees include:

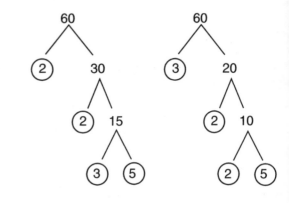

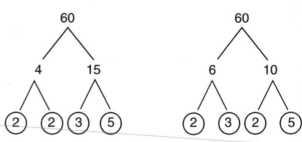

7. 15. Possible strategies include listing all the multiples of 3 less than 20 (3, 6, 9, 12, 15, 18), scratching off the even multiples of three (6, 12, and 18), then scratching off the square numbers and the prime numbers (9 and 3). Only the number 15 remains.

*Answers and/or discussion are included in the Lesson Guide.

**Answers for all the Home Practice in the *Discovery Assignment Book* are at the end of the unit.

LESSON GUIDE 5

Product Bingo

Estimated Class Sessions: 1

Students learn about products and factors in a game that reviews and practices multiplication facts.

Key Content

- Solving problems involving multiples, factors, and primes.
- Practicing the multiplication facts.
- Explaining mathematical reasoning.

Key Vocabulary

factor
product

Materials List

Print Materials for Students

	Math Facts and Daily Practice and Problems	Game	Homework	Written Assessment
Student Books				
Student Guide		*Product Bingo* Pages 116–117		
Discovery Assignment Book		*Product Bingo Game Boards* Page 49	Home Practice Part 3 Page 40	
Teacher Resources				
Facts Resource Guide	DPP Item 4S			DPP Item 4S *Quiz on 2s and 3s*
Unit Resource Guide	DPP Items S–T Pages 20–21 ◎			DPP Item S *Quiz on 2s and 3s* Page 20 ◎
Generic Section ◎		*Small Multiplication Tables,* 1 per student (to tape on desk)		

◎ *available on Teacher Resource CD*

All Transparency Masters, Blackline Masters, and Assessment Blackline Masters in the Unit Resource Guide are on the Teacher Resource CD.

Supplies for Each Student

clear plastic spinner (or a pencil and paper clip)
small objects such as beans to use as markers

Materials for the Teacher

Observational Assessment Record (Unit Resource Guide, Pages 7–8 and Teacher Resource CD)
Individual Assessment Record Sheet (Teacher Implementation Guide, Assessment section and Teacher Resource CD)

Developing the Activity

Product Bingo is a game that requires solving many multiplication fact problems and provides another context for discussing solution strategies. Analyzing the cards that are most likely to win gives students an opportunity to apply what they have learned about factors.

Begin by discussing the rules on the *Product Bingo* Game Pages in the *Student Guide*. Each group should select a Caller who will spin the spinners and call out the two numbers. The other four players choose a game board on the *Product Bingo Game Boards* page in the *Discovery Assignment Book*.

All the students in each group should find the products and place a marker on the product if it is on their board. The Caller keeps a list of the problems and the answers by writing multiplication sentences such as $3 \times 2 = 6$. (The 3 and the 2 are the numbers the Caller spun.) The first player to get four markers in a row or a marker in each corner is the winner.

Ask students to play *Product Bingo* for 30 minutes. If they finish a game before that time, they may start another game with a different student acting as caller. Have players trade boards before they start a second game. If students are in the middle of a game when time is called, ask them to decide if they can determine a winner.

🌀 TIMS Tip

If you do not have clear plastic spinners, students can use a pencil and a paper clip as shown in Figure 8 in Lesson 3.

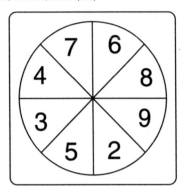

Product Bingo

This is a game for five players. You need a clear plastic spinner and beans or something else to use as markers. If you don't have a spinner, you can use a pencil and a paper clip.

One player is the Caller. The other players each choose a game board from the *Product Bingo Game Boards* Game Page in the *Discovery Assignment Book*.

The Caller spins the spinner twice. If the product of the spun digits is on your game board, then put a marker on it. The Caller should keep track of all digits spun by writing multiplication sentences on a piece of paper.

The first player with four markers in a row or a marker in each corner is the winner. (The **P** space, for **Product**, is a free space.)

116 SG · Grade 4 · Unit 4 · Lesson 5   **Product Bingo**

Student Guide - Page 116

Name _____   Date _____

Product Bingo Game Boards

Board 1

40	72	10	35
42	28	20	27
15	45	P	6
30	48	14	56

Board 3

8	24	27	54
20	12	21	32
36	P	14	45
63	18	72	16

Board 2

9	P	22	81
64	13	25	32
15	14	56	29
7	10	4	49

Board 4

4	45	25	81
49	56	6	32
9	64	P	10
15	8	42	48

Copyright © Kendall/Hunt Publishing Company

Product Bingo   DAB · Grade 4 · Unit 4 · Lesson 5   49

Discovery Assignment Book - Page 49

Answer these questions after you have played *Product Bingo*.

1. Which game board is the best?
2. Which game board is the worst?
3. Why is the best game board better than the worst one?
4. Design your own *Product Bingo* game board.
    A. First, draw an empty game board:

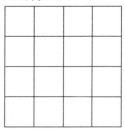

    B. Second, write products of the numbers 2 through 9 in all the squares except one.
    C. Finally, put a **P** in the last square.
5. Play *Product Bingo* using your game board. Did you win or not? Explain why.

Product Bingo   SG · Grade 4 · Unit 4 · Lesson 5   117

Student Guide - Page 117

The questions on the *Product Bingo* Game Pages in the *Student Guide* help structure a discussion of the game strategies and factors. When students answer the questions, they should compare all four boards. Board 3 is the best board because it has five products (18, 12, 24, 36, and 16) that can be obtained in more than one way. Board 2 can never win because 22, 13, 29, and 7 will never be products with the given spinner, so that four in a row is not possible. The other boards are in-between, with Board 1 being slightly better than Board 4.

If students have difficulty deciding which board has the greatest chance of winning the game, encourage them to examine the numbers on the boards closely. Prompt students to examine the factors of the numbers on each board. The board that is most likely to win is the board whose numbers have the greatest number of factors that are on the spinner. For example, Board 2 has the number 13 on it. 13 has two factors, 1 and itself. The factors, 1 and 13, are not on the spinner, so the number 13 on Board 2 can never be filled in. However, a number like 12 on Board 3 can be filled in by spinning 2 and 6 or 3 and 4.

Students can write the possible factors for each number on the boards (keeping the numbers on the spinner in mind) to find the board that is most likely to win. Once students determine the board that is the best or the worst, they are prepared to design their own game board as described in *Question 4.*

Suggestions for Teaching the Lesson

Homework and Practice

- Encourage students to play *Product Bingo* at home. Students will need their game pages from the *Student Guide* and the *Discovery Assignment Book*. They may use a pencil and a paper clip as a spinner.

- Assign some or all of the word problems in Lesson 6 *Multiplying to Solve Problems* for homework.

- Assign Part 3 of the Home Practice. Part 3 contains word problems that provide practice in computation and math facts.

Answers for Part 3 of the Home Practice can be found in the Answer Key at the end of this lesson and at the end of this unit.

Assessment

- Use DPP Bit S to assess students' fluency with the multiplication facts for the twos and threes.

- Use the *Observational Assessment Record* to record students' fluency with the multiplication facts. Also document students' abilities to explain their reasoning as they tell the class why one *Product Bingo* card is better than another.

- Transfer appropriate documentation from the Unit 4 *Observational Assessment Record* to the students' *Individual Assessment Record Sheets*.

Extension

DPP Challenge T is an exercise in which students collect data, find medians, and answer questions about their work.

Daily Practice and Problems: Challenge for Lesson 5

T. Challenge: You Are Breathtaking! (URG p. 21)

Work with a partner. With a stopwatch or by watching the second hand on a clock, you and your partner will time how long each of you can hold your breath. Collect data from at least 8 students.

1. What is the median time for your data?

2. By how many seconds does your time differ from the median time?

3. Name some of the variables that may affect how long a person can hold his or her breath.

Name _____ Date _____

Part 3 Working at the Grocery Store

Choose an appropriate tool to help you solve each of the problems. Use a picture, paper and pencil, or a calculator. Show how you solved each problem.

1. Keenya's sister, Shenika, works at a grocery store. Today she is stocking shelves. She stacks soup cans three cans high. If she makes 6 stacks, how many soup cans will she shelve?

2. Shenika brings in some shopping carts from the parking lot. She makes 4 rows of carts. She tries to place the same number of carts in each row. If she brings in 17 carts, how many carts can she place in each row?

3. Shenika gets paid six dollars an hour. Last week she worked 15 hours. How much did she earn?

4. When Shenika works the cash register on a Saturday, she works nonstop. In the express line, customers may purchase only 10 items or less. When working the express line, she can ring up about 5 customers in 15 minutes. If she works a 6-hour day, about how many customers can she serve?

5. The grocery bill for one of Shenika's customers is $15.52. The customer gives Shenika $20.02. How much change should the customer receive?

6. Grapes are on sale for 69¢ a pound. How much do 3 pounds of grapes cost?

7. For every $3 a customer spends at the grocery store, he or she gets a stamp that can be used for purchasing dishes. One customer bought groceries for herself and an elderly neighbor. The two separate bills were $43 and $28. How many stamps should this customer receive for herself and her neighbor?

40 DAB · Grade 4 · Unit 4   PRODUCTS AND FACTORS

Discovery Assignment Book - Page 40

AT A GLANCE

Math Facts and Daily Practice and Problems

DPP S is a quiz on the multiplication facts for the twos and threes. DPP Challenge T practices finding medians.

Developing the Activity

1. Discuss the rules of the game using the *Product Bingo* Game Pages.
2. Model the game.
3. Students play the game.
4. Students answer *Questions 1–5* on the *Product Bingo* Game Pages in the *Student Guide.*

Homework

1. Students play the game at home.
2. Assign word problems in Lesson 6 for homework.
3. Assign Part 3 of the Home Practice.

Assessment

1. DPP Bit S is a multiplication facts quiz.
2. Use the *Observational Assessment Record* to record students' proficiency finding products playing the game. Also document students' abilities to explain their reasoning as they tell the class why one Product Bingo card is better.
3. Transfer appropriate documentation from the Unit 4 *Observational Assessment Record* to the *Individual Assessment Record Sheets.*

Notes:

Student Guide

Questions 1–5 (SG p. 117)

*1. Board 3

*2. Board 2

*3. Answers will vary. Board 3 has five products that can be obtained in more than one way.

*4. Boards will vary.

5. Answers will vary.

Discovery Assignment Book

**Home Practice (DAB p. 40)

Part 3. Working at the Grocery Store

Questions 1–7

1. 18 cans. 6 stacks $\times$ 3 cans per stack = 18 cans.

2. 4 carts in three rows and 5 carts in one row. 17 carts $\div$ 4 carts per row = 4 carts per row with 1 left over.

3. $90.00. $6.00 per hour $\times$ 15 hours = $90.00.

4. 120 customers. 5 customers in 15 minutes is the same as 20 customers in one hour. 20 customers per hour $\times$ 6 hours = 120 customers.

5. $4.50. $20.02 − $15.52 = $4.50

6. $2.07. $0.69 $\times$ 3 = $2.07

7. 23 stamps. $43.00 + $28.00 = $71.00 $71.00 $\div$ 3 = 23 remainder 2.

*Answers and/or discussion are included in the Lesson Guide.

**Answers for all the Home Practice in the *Discovery Assignment Book* are at the end of the unit.

OPTIONAL LESSON

There are no Daily Practice and Problems items for this lesson.

LESSON GUIDE 6

Multiplying to Solve Problems

Estimated Class Sessions: 1

This lesson is a series of word problems requiring multiplication computations. To solve them, students choose whether to use paper and pencil, calculators, multiplication tables, mental math, or manipulatives.

Key Content

*   Solving multistep word problems using multiplication and division.
*   Choosing appropriate methods and tools to calculate (calculator, paper and pencil, mental math, or estimation).
*   Connecting mathematics to real-life situations.
*   Communicating solutions verbally and in writing.

Materials List

Print Materials for Students

		Optional Activity
Student Book	**Student Guide**	*Multiplying to Solve Problems* Page 118
Teacher Resource	**Generic Section** ⊙	*Small Multiplication Tables* 1 per student (to tape on desk)

⊙ *available on Teacher Resource CD*

All Transparency Masters, Blackline Masters, and Assessment Blackline Masters in the Unit Resource Guide are on the Teacher Resource CD.

Supplies for Each Student Group

calculators
50 square-inch tiles

Developing the Activity

Knowledge of factors and multiples is a useful asset for solving the problems in this lesson. A goal for students is to develop the ability to analyze a problem critically and choose an appropriate method for solving it. No one method will be the most efficient or most effective for every problem. Students must learn to approach each problem flexibly to avoid applying a memorized algorithm or tool mechanically, without considering its appropriateness to the problem at hand.

Using Tools. As students become more fluent with the multiplication and division facts, the facts will become an increasingly important part of their problem-solving repertoire. Until then, students have the option of referring to their multiplication tables or using calculators. Students may also choose to work with manipulatives or drawings, use mental math, or paper and pencil. All of these options are good problem-solving tools and should be used by students where appropriate. For further information about word problem sets, see the TIMS Tutor: *Word Problems* in the *Teacher Implementation Guide*.

Using the Problems. The problems can be used in several ways. Students can work on the problems individually, in pairs, or in groups. One approach is to ask students to work on the problems individually at first and then to come together in pairs or small groups to compare solutions. Then the group's solutions can be shared with others in a class discussion. The problems can also be assigned for homework. Because this activity does not require much teacher preparation, it is appropriate to leave for a substitute teacher.

Suggestions for Teaching the Lesson

Homework and Practice

Assign some or all of the problems on the *Multiplying to Solve Problems* Activity Page for homework.

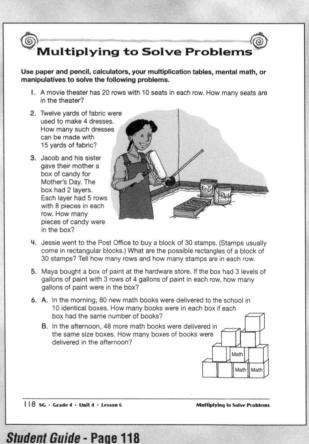

Multiplying to Solve Problems

Use paper and pencil, calculators, your multiplication tables, mental math, or manipulatives to solve the following problems.

1. A movie theater has 20 rows with 10 seats in each row. How many seats are in the theater?

2. Twelve yards of fabric were used to make 4 dresses. How many such dresses can be made with 15 yards of fabric?

3. Jacob and his sister gave their mother a box of candy for Mother's Day. The box had 2 layers. Each layer had 5 rows with 8 pieces in each row. How many pieces of candy were in the box?

4. Jessie went to the Post Office to buy a block of 30 stamps. (Stamps usually come in rectangular blocks.) What are the possible rectangles of a block of 30 stamps? Tell how many rows and how many stamps are in each row.

5. Maya bought a box of paint at the hardware store. If the box had 3 levels of gallons of paint with 3 rows of 4 gallons of paint in each row, how many gallons of paint were in the box?

6. A. In the morning, 80 new math books were delivered to the school in 10 identical boxes. How many books were in each box if each box had the same number of books?

   B. In the afternoon, 48 more math books were delivered in the same size boxes. How many boxes of books were delivered in the afternoon?

118 SG · Grade 4 · Unit 4 · Lesson 6   **Multiplying to Solve Problems**

Student Guide - Page 118

AT A GLANCE

Developing the Activity

1. Students solve problems on the *Multiplying to Solve Problems* Activity Page in the *Student Guide.*
2. Students discuss solutions and solution paths.

Homework

Assign some or all of the problems for homework.

Notes:

Student Guide

Questions 1–6 (SG p. 118)

1. 200 seats, 20 rows $\times$ 10 seats per row = 200 seats.

2. 5 dresses; 12 yards $\div$ 4 dresses = 3 yards per dress, 15 yards $\div$ 3 yards per dress = 5 dresses.

3. 80 pieces of candy, $2 \times 5 \times 8 = 80$.

4. Possible rectangles include: 1 row of 30 stamps, 2 rows of 15 stamps, 3 rows of 10 stamps, 5 rows of 6 stamps. The rows and numbers of stamps in each row can be exchanged to make blocks that are turned, but these rectangles are the same as those listed.

5. 36 gallons of paint, $3 \times 3 \times 4 = 36$.

6. **A.** 8 books, 80 books $\div$ 10 boxes = 8 books per box.

    B. 6 boxes, 48 books $\div$ 8 books per box = 6 boxes.

*Answers and/or discussion are included in the Lesson Guide.
**Answers for all the Home Practice in the *Discovery Assignment Book* are at the end of the unit.

<u>Discovery Assignment Book</u>

Home Practice

Part 2. Multiplication: Factors, Multiples, Primes, and Squares

Questions 1–6 (DAB p. 39)

1. Yes. Explanations will vary. One possible explanation is that 34 is an even number and all even numbers are multiples of 2.

2. No. Explanations will vary. Possible explanations: 1, 5, 7, and 35 are the factors of 35. 3 does not divide evenly into 35.

3. Answers will vary. All even numbers: 2, 4, 6, 8, 10, 12, 14, 16, 18 . . .

4. Answers will vary. All multiples of 3: 3, 6, 9, 12, 15, 18, 21, 24 . . .

5. Yes. Explanations will vary. One possible explanation is that 7 has no other factors but 1 and itself.

6. **A.** 25
   B. 100
   C. 4
   D. 9

Part 3. Working at the Grocery Store

Questions 1–7 (DAB p. 40)

1. 18 cans. 6 stacks $\times$ 3 cans per stack = 18 cans.

2. 4 carts in three rows and 5 carts in one row. 17 carts $\div$ 4 carts per row = 4 carts per row with 1 left over.

3. $90.00. $6.00 per hour $\times$ 15 hours = $90.00.

4. 120 customers. 5 customers in 15 minutes is the same as 20 customers in one hour. 20 customers per hour $\times$ 6 hours = 120 customers.

5. $4.50. $20.02 $-$ $15.52 = $4.50

6. $2.07. $0.69 $\times$ 3 = $2.07

7. 23 stamps. $43.00 + $28.00 = $71.00 $71.00 $\div$ 3 = 23 remainder 2.

*Answers and/or discussion are included in the Lesson Guide.